Dedication:

The inspiration for this book comes from all of you, my wonderful, loyal customers and friends.

THE BEST
OF ADRIEN ARPEL:

BEAUTY ADVICE,

HOME REMEDIES,

AND TIPS

Published by Endeavour Group, U.K., 85 Larkhall Rise, London, SW4 6HR

ISBN: 1-873913-08-7

First Printing   April 1996

10 9 8 7 6 5 4 3 2 1

CONTENTS

INTRO

Dear Reader:

Let's face it. The one thing all women share, whether we're standing in front of a Hollywood camera, crying at our child's high school graduation or attending our 30-plus high school reunion, is the desire to hear these welcome words:

"You look fantastic! What have you done to yourself?"

For that tiny sub-culture of women consisting of voluptuous movie stars and wraith-thin supermodels, the answer would be a laundry list of pampering routines from the expensive (complete facelift) to the do-able inexpensive but little known beauty secrets their agents ferret out from high-priced beauty consultants and personal trainers.

The results: The older these women get, the better and younger they look. Now, I'm not saying the right beauty tricks will keep them (or you) looking like a teen queen (and if you're like me, you wouldn't want to go back and have to do all you've done all over again!), but a little professional know-how can keep you looking terrific no matter what your age.

And I should know! I'm not some natural beauty who decided to sell cosmetics when my Miss America reign was up. I've been a beauty professional for over thirty years, starting my own company way-back when, out of a desire to look better myself. I knew I could never be a Catherine Deneuve clone no matter how hard I tried, and I resented the high-pressure cosmetics salesgirls telling me they could wave their mascara wands and redo my chromosome structure making me into a perfect beauty. (If that would have worked, I would be on the silver screen making eyes at Warren Beatty—and have you noticed he doesn't seem to look any older, either?)

When, after much experimenting, I learned how to make myself look better by approaching the beauty biz with realistic expectations, I took $400 dollars I had earned baby-sitting and started my own company at the age of seventeen. (I still sometimes wonder where I got the nerve.) My goal: to help other women who were also interested in sound products, not empty promises. And enough women have agreed with me to help *Adrien Arpel, Inc.* grow beyond my greatest expectations ... we are now located in hundreds of the finest department stores in the United States and Canada.

As part of spreading my philosophy—look like yourself, only better and younger—I hold seminars in most of these stores, do regular guest appearances on *Live with Regis and Kathie Lee*, meet thousands of women with beauty problems and questions like yours, and answer as many as I can face to face. I also work with the models and actresses who use my products, and am privy to their personal look-younger tricks.

And, of course, I count among my friends many dermatologists, hair stylists, and cosmetic chemists whom I shamelessly badger into revealing what works, what is hype and how to take the newest breakthroughs and put them into products my special customers can buy without taking out a second mortgage on their house. (Sorry, ladies, that means no sheep placenta for you . . . but you know that placenta is best kept with the sheep!)

The result of my asking the beauty pros the questions you ask me are both good and bad:

THE BAD NEWS: Experts run away from me when they see me at cocktail parties, leaving me too much free time to over-indulge in hors-d'oevres.

THE GOOD NEWS: I have voluminous notebooks filled with facts and tips that I turned into three best-selling beauty books: *Adrien Arpel's 3-Week Crash Makeover/Shapeover Beauty Program; How to Look Ten Years Younger; Adrien Arpel's 851 Fast Beauty Fixes and Facts.*

One reason my books sold so well was I took to heart the oft-mentioned remark from my customers: "I wish I could take you home with me!" So I did the next best thing: I put "me" and my results-oriented advice within the covers of my books.

Since my association with the television shopping channel, I'm proud to say I am meeting so many more women that I might not have had the pleasure of knowing: You, the television viewer, from chatting with you on the air, reading your letters and listening to your comments on my 800 phone number, I've learned what warm—and loyal—girlfriends and customers you are. And, how cosmetics-savvy you are, too.

When I heard the questions you asked about looking better, looking younger, staving off the superficial signs of aging which really don't have to appear so soon (Look at me: I'm a grandma and proud of it, but I certainly don't look the way my grandmother did), I decided just what to give you to say "thank you" for your support. I've gathered my most important anti-aging, beauty-boosting tricks and tips and put them together in the enclosed book, *The Best of Adrien Arpel*, just for you.

But to get the most benefit from *The Best of Adrien Arpel*, you must make as many of the suggestions as practicable part of your beauty routine. I want you to consider this a work manual as well as a chat with me, and use the information herein that has made so many hundreds of thousands of women of all ages better friends with their mirrors.

Read this book and remember *AGE IS JUST A NUMBER.*

Love,
Adrien

CHAPTER ONE
S.O.S. . . . SAVE OUR SKIN

If you want the skin of an 18-year-old prom queen, and you're well past the age of consent, I'm afraid I can't help you! My beauty philosophy is based on scientific fact, not science fiction. And though my treatments and tips will help you look younger and better, I'm not powerful enough to go one-on-one with Mother Nature. She's one savvy lady, and She insists that first bloom of youth be reserved for the very young.

But, guess what? You can have fantastic-looking skin that won't give away your age if you know how to take care of your complexion . . . and that's where I come in. I can show you how to keep your face looking like a luscious grape, rather than a dried-up raisin, *no mean feat.*

So make yourself a cup of coffee, and follow along as I show you how to become your own skin expert. I'm cheaper and quicker than a plastic surgeon—and lots less painful!

First, a few skin facts. The skin is a complicated organ (the largest in your body). When you study your face in a mirror, your skin looks flat and solid, but it's really a complicated multi-layered network. The epidermis is the outer layer; its keratinized protein protects your skin's inner layers against environmental attack, and manufactures new cells. The dermis, or inner layer, contains collagen and elastin, oil and sweat glands, hair follicles, etc.

To give yourself the best-looking epidermis on the block, you have to interface your face with the bounty of treatments provided by Mother Nature's stepdaughters, the cosmetics wizards.

SIX STEPS TO YOUNGER LOOKING SKIN

Cosmetics companies spend big advertising bucks to help you understand how their products work, but you'll be able to decipher the fine print easily if you can grasp one simple concept: all treatment products fall into one of six categories, so your treatment plan will contain a mix of the following six steps:

STEP #1: MAKEUP REMOVING

Melts cosmetics off of your face without excessive tugging and scrubbing via a modern formulation cold creme base.

STEP #2: CLEANSING

Removes pollutants, dirt, excessive oils. Deep cleanses pores, dislodges impurities, and refines skin texture.

STEP #3: TONING AND FIRMING

Tightens and tones skin following cleansing, acts as a skin rinse, sops up oil overflow. Can be called astringent/toner/freshener, depending on the manufacturer. The more powerful toners contain alcohol, which may or may not be too strong for your skin. Also in this category are serum-based elastic lifts that tighten and firm sagging skin on throat and breasts as well as face.

STEP #4: EXFOLIATING

Removes top layer of dry, dead skin cells, exposing younger-looking, softer surface skin. Formulas include mildly abrasive cremes imbedded with cleansing grains (i.e., almonds, oatmeal, flower extracts), or vegetable peel-offs.

STEP #5: NOURISHING AND BALANCING

Keep skin looking and feeling supple, diminish dryness, shield the skin from the elements and seal in its own natural moisture, and provide a cushion for your makeup. These treatment cremes/moisturizers are used day and/or night. They may contain special ingredients like collagen protein, Alpha Hydroxy acids, vitamins, flower and plant extracts, or SPF sun protection factor. Special treatments for eyes, lips, lines and wrinkles fall into this category.

STEP #6: MASKS

Put the "treat" in beauty treatment. Unlike the products mentioned in the last classification, these are deep nourishers and tighteners you spread on and leave on for three to ten minutes. They clarify and refine oily skin; velvetize dry skin. Choose your mask according to your skin type and what you're trying to accomplish. Oily skins thrive with mud masks; other skins might favor a milk protein and flower petal combo. Some masks harden, some stay soft—there are cremes, gels, collagen masks—whatever suits your fancy. The common denominator: they feel *sooo* good.

How do you fit these six skin-saving steps into your schedule? First you must know what type of skin you're in. (And don't worry, it takes longer to read about the steps then to do them; I know you don't have hours to spend on your face.)

KNOW YOUR SKIN TYPE

Before you learn how to improve, maintain or retrieve your skin's youthful glow, you must know what kind of skin you're in today. Don't be surprised if it's changed in the last five years; look at the rest of your body!

Here are two quick ways to type yourself:

TEST ONE: STRIP IT. Take a thin brown paper bag (a child's lunch bag), cut some strips, and before washing your face in the morning, rub one strip back and forth against your forehead, another over your chin and nose. Swipe a third across your cheeks. Is the paper shiny, or so oily it's almost translucent? You have oily skin. If the strip rubbed over your cheeks comes clean, and the rest is shiny, you have combination skin. The paper looks clean enough to rewrap your husband's lunch? Spring for a fresh bag, but understand you have dry skin.

TEST TWO: TIME IT. Cleanse your face, wait fifteen minutes, then press brown strip over nose, forehead and chin area, the "oily T zone." If there's shiny residue, you have oily skin. No oil? Wait another 45 minutes. If it takes that long to develop a slight sheen on the paper, you have normal skin. If a few hours go by and your paper is still dry, you have dry skin.

Here are a few more objective clues to defining skin type:

YOU'RE OIL RICH IF:

* ★ Your face always looks shiny, and downright greasy around the nose.
* ★ As the hours pass, your chin and forehead get that slippery feel, even under makeup.
* ★ No matter what your age, you still get occasional blackheads and enlarged pores.
* ★ Your skin feels bumpy to the touch.

YOU'RE A DRY DAME IF:

- ★ Your skin feels like it's one size too small.
- ★ Fine lines and laugh lines started showing up before your thirtieth birthday.
- ★ In cold weather your skin gets flaky, feels ready to crack.

YOU HAVE NORMAL SKIN IF:

- ★ Your skin feels soft, supple and rarely breaks out.
- ★ Skin "fits comfortably," looks well with just a dollop of moisturizer and a kiss of blusher.

Congratulations on being normal. (And you thought only your psychiatrist would say that!) You picked the right parents. But once you hit 25, even normal skin starts to head the way of the dinosaur. It will tend to dry out, so for purposes of treatment, align yourself with dry-skinned women.

LOOK YOUNGER FACE MAINTENANCE GUIDE

Application Note: When you apply any cremes and cleansers, do so with upward and outward strokes of your hands. You'll turn your daily routine into a youth-lifting massage. Downward strokes work with gravity to drag your face down.

MAKEUP REMOVAL

If you're like me, and you would sooner forget your car keys than your foundation, mascara and blusher, you must pay special (but quick) attention to makeup removal. Before you cleanse at night, no matter what your skin type, you need a modern version of "cold creme" type remover (I prefer one with a coconut base) to dislodge the day's face wardrobe. Apply with fingertips, leave creme in place while you brush your teeth so it has time to "melt" the makeup, then tissue off or remove with a wet washcloth. Pat, *don't pull*, the cloth. Tugging promotes wrinkling. Now, follow the regimen for your complexion.

OILY SKIN: BEDTIME

- ◆ Use a makeup melt to melt off makeup and flush out daily grime and pollution. Let makeup melt sit on your face for at least one minute. Remove with hot, wet washcloth. (Heat helps unclog oil trapped in pores.)

◆ If skin is broken out, use a cleanser containing mild abrasives (i.e., sea kelp, almonds, oatmeal, minerals, pumice, flower extracts).

◆ Spray face with a mix of 1/2 astringent, 1/2 mineral water to tone skin, help tighten the look of enlarged pores, and blot excess oils.

◆ Apply night time eye gel or a line softening stick (creme or oil may slide onto your breakout areas).

◆ Apply nourishing skin correction creme every night.

OILY SKIN: DAYTIME

◆ Cleanse with gentle daily cleanser containing mild abrasives (i.e., sea kelp, flower particles, flower petals).

◆ Saturate a cotton pad with astringent and apply all over face and neck.

◆ Apply a lightweight day creme. (*Skin Correction Complex Four-Cremes-in-One* can be used.)

NORMAL-TO-DRY SKIN: BEDTIME

◆ Remove makeup with makeup melt after letting the creme sit on your skin at least one minute. Use a wash cloth soaked in tepid, not hot, water to gently remove creme/cosmetic residue, or tissue off.

◆ For deeper cleansing, wet face and lather on foaming soap-replacement cleanser with fingertips.

◆ Fully remove either type of cleanser by holding a tepid wash cloth against face, then rinse with cool water.

◆ Super-hydrate clean skin with your favorite commercial freshener or a combination of 1/2 mineral water and 1/2 alcohol free toner. Spritz well, leave face damp.

◆ Gently pat eye gel into place on both upper and lower lids.

◆ With skin still damp, apply nourishing night creme (or my *Four-In-One Creme with Alpha Hydroxy*) to face and throat. (You're using upward and outward strokes, right?)

◆ Night creme note: Just 1/4 teaspoon of a good quality night creme will cover your face and throat, so you're not squandering a queen's ransom each time you nourish your skin.

NORMAL-TO-DRY SKIN: DAYTIME

- Cleanse with an energizing deep cleansing agent and splash with cool water.

- Tone with your favorite non-alcoholic freshener or a mix of flower water and mineral water. Wipe all over face and throat with cotton pad, or mist directly on face.

- Add your nourishing day creme followed by a moisturizer to seal the creme in place. (or, use my *Four-In-One Creme*. I'm not trying to plug *Four-In-One* here, but so many hundreds of thousands of you already have it, I'm afraid some of you may think it shouldn't be part of your daily regimen!)

You'll notice that I've left exfoliating and "masking" off of your daily routine. You'll have to adapt how often you include these steps to your individual skin's texture and condition. Your skin may need exfoliating two to three times a week.

You may want to use a mask once a week, or alternate your favorite masks during the week. The response of your own skin (and the amount of free time you can generate) will determine the best frequency for you.

Now that you're an expert on daily/weekly face care, you think your job is done? Alas, there are other skin agers lurking about, and I'm going to tell you how to deal with them.

AGER #1: COLLAGEN BREAKDOWN

Collagen and elastin are two proteins that form the connective tissue physically supporting your face. As you age, the collagen becomes less elastic and all the smiling and grimacing, frowning and fretting you do no longer reverts back to a smooth canvas when you return to a placid expression. Why? Because your collagen loses much of that elastic "bounce back" ability. The result: permanent lines and sagging.

SOLUTIONS

- Increase your vitamin C intake. C produces collagen; add a 100 mg C supplement, as well as plenty of citrus fruits, to your diet.
- Avoid the sun as much as possible. The drying, burning and peeling you see on the outside is only half the story. Sun is a collagen

destroyer, needlessly robbing your skin of the support system it needs to look young. (More on sun later.)

- Wear a "scaffold" for your skin in the form of an Instant Face Lift. The scaffold for the face is the *Skinlastic Lift*. Temporary lifts stay in place until you wash them off, and also have cumulative tightening benefits with continuous use.

- Use a creme that contains collagen and/or Alpha Hydroxy acids. Collagen protein is the major component of the skin's connective tissues; it keeps water in the skin, thus strengthening elasticity. Alpha Hydroxy acids help cast off dead, dry cells, providing skin renewal, improved tone and heightened elasticity and firmness. "AHAS" mimic the wrinkle reduction effects of Retin-A, minus the irritation. This newest category of skin savers softens the appearance of wrinkles and lines . . . you'll be hearing more about Alpha Hydroxy acids in the future.

AGER #2: MOISTURE LOSS

The surface of your skin is bathed in oils, sweat and other good secretions that not only keep the water within your skin's cells from evaporating, they also keep external pollutants from penetrating. As your skin passes the quarter century milestone, this protective layer (the so-called acid mantle) starts to malfunction and your skin starts drying up because the water within evaporates.

SOLUTIONS

- Replace lost moisture and lock it in your skin. The moisture we're talking about is water, so leave your skin damp after you wash your face, and cover the "water" with a moisturizer, which actually serves as a water-loss barrier. (Note: Because youth-giving moisture is related to water, not oil, oily-skinned women must use a moisturizer, too.)

- Spray your face with water as often as you can during the day to rehydrate. You can even "spritz" right over your makeup. I keep my spritzer bottle handy on my desk. After all, you mist your plants; doesn't your skin deserve equal treatment?

- If you wore long hair during the Age of Aquarius, it's now time to pray to Aquarius, the water sign. Drink plenty of water, Nature's miracle fluid, six to eight glasses a day. It's one of the supermodels' beauty secrets we can all share. At a beauty shoot you will see all the models have one thing in common (besides legs that seem longer than my entire body): They're always toting around bottles of *Evian* water, forever sipping the H$_2$O. Drinking water plumps your skin from the inside out, and plain old tapwater will do just fine, the harder the better. Ask your town water commission if you have hard (mineral rich) or soft water. I jazz my water up with some lemon or lime slices. It makes me think I'm having something more elegant to drink. I call it my "skin cocktail".

♦ When you cleanse, make your skin's final rinse in cool or cold water. Hot water opens the pores, letting the moisture leak out.

♦ When the heat goes on, plug in your humidifier. You needn't be a baby with croup to benefit from the little misting machine. Central heating dries your complexion, parching your skin as well as your throat. A humidifier returns to the air the moisture heat robs. Lots of plants help, too. So does sleeping a la Scandinavians: keep the thermostat low, pile on the blankets and open the window a crack if you can bear it. Cold is Nature's preservative.

AGER #3: PALE, COLORLESS, LIFELESS SKIN

A radiant, healthy glow is definitely a sign of youth. If you've checked with your doctor and that dull, dreary look is not due to a medical problem, it's probably poor circulation of the blood vessels under the skin. While you can't increase blood flow, you can stimulate it and simulate that pink, rosy glow of good health . . . and youth.

SOLUTIONS

♦ **PERFORM FACIAL MASSAGE.** There's no better way to both stimulate your skin and relax your psyche than facial manipulation; it's the hands-on, hands-down favorite part of every professional salon facial. A good facial massage will soften tension lines and improve circulation, turning on a healthy glow. But you mustn't even consider facial massage or exercises without the proper massage oil. A lubricant is necessary to help your fingers slide across your skin without doing any damage.

Use one of my botanical essential oil combinations such as *Pure Energy Oil, Peace, Tranquility, and Stress Relief Oil*, or *Pleasant Dreams Oil*. Or, make one yourself right at home. Botanical extracts are available in all health food stores.

Here's my favorite at home recipe; it is a balancing formula that is good for massaging all skin types. Mix 1/2 cup of sunflower oil, 1/2 tablespoon of avocado oil, 25 drops of lavender oil, and 16 drops of bergamot oil. Make sure to store it in a tightly covered, dark-colored glass container.

Now, follow the step-by-step instructions. It will take awhile to get your fingers positioned correctly, but once you understand the technique, the massage should take about five minutes.

1. Linear movement over forehead. Place your hands at the hairline, your right hand above and to the right of your right eye; your left hand above and to the left of your left eye. Slide your fingertips to the temples with pressure on the upward stroke. Slide to the end of the eyebrow; then stroke to the hairline across the forehead and back.

2. Circular movements over forehead. Start at eyebrow line and work across the middle of the forehead; then stroke towards the hairline above the brow.

3. Criss-cross movements. Start at one side of the forehead and work towards the middle of the forehead and then towards the hairline.

4. Chin movement. Lift chin with thumbs, using slight pressure.

5. Lower cheek movements. Use circular motion, going from chin to ear and rotate.

6. Mouth, nose and cheek movements. Use fingertips in circular motions, moving along chin from the ear, up and around the mouth, continuing upwards towards the bridge of the nose, back down the sides of the nose and on the upper cheekbone under the eyes.

7. Stroking forehead movements. Slide fingers, palm contoured to the forehead, to the center of the forehead. Then draw your fingers, using slight pressure, towards the temples and rotate from the hairline to the outer tip of the brows.

8. Brow and eye area movements. Place the middle fingers slightly above the inner corner of eyes, slide to the outer corner of the eyes; then under the eyes, back to the starting point.

9. Nose and upper cheek movements. Slide fingers down the nose, along the sides. Using gentle rotary movements, move across the cheeks to the temples. Slide the fingers back to the bridge of the nose, sliding under the eyes and upwards along the sides of the nose.

10. Mouth and nose movements. Apply circular motions with fingers from corner of mouth up the sides of the face. Slide the fingers over the brows and down to the corners of the mouth.

11. Lip and chin movements. Draw the fingers from the center of the upper lip, around the mouth, going under lower lip and around the chin.

12. Lifting movements of cheeks. Proceed from chin to ear lobe; then from mouth to ears; next from nose to top of ears.

13. The rotary movement. Proceed from chin to ear lobes; mouth to middle of ears; nose to top of ears.

14. Light tapping movement on cheeks. On one side of face, using both hands, massage from chin to bottom of ear; mouth to middle of ear; nose to top of ear; massage across forehead and repeat the first three steps on the other side of the face.

15. Stroking movement for neck. Massage with firm strokes, upward and outward.

16. Circular movement over neck and chest. Starting at the back of the ears, using rotary motions, move down the side of the neck, cross-over slide the hands to the outer edge of the shoulder, circle across the upper chest to the center; cross-over hands and circle upwards to the end of the bone.

17. Place hands behind neck so fingertips meet. Massage back of neck with fingers, sides of neck with gentle thumb pressure.

- **EXFOLIATE.** As you get older the rate at which new, young, healthy skin cells push their way to the top slows down, meaning that top, gray layer of epidermis hangs around longer than it should. To speed up the process of bringing new, pink cells to the top, we have to remove the youth-blocking layer, and we accomplish that by sloughing or exfoliating.

  You can use a gritty cleanser containing nature based abrasives (like dried flower parts, cornmeal, sea kelp, or almonds), and skin softeners (honey, oils) housed in a creme base. Or, you can use a product designed to help peel the top layer. Whether you apply these exfoliants with your fingertips (to wet skin) or a mechanical brush like the one with a skin activating machine, you will see younger, more alive looking skin left behind when you remove that old, dead layer.

- If you've run out of sloughing grains, put 1/2 teaspoon of powdered ginseng or 1/2 teaspoon soya granules into one tablespoon of face or cold creme. Apply to damp skin, especially blemished areas, in small, gentle circular motions.

- After cleansing, mix 1/2 cup buttermilk with 2 teaspoons of lemon juice, and apply with cotton ball. Leave on for fifteen minutes. Both ingredients have mild bleaching properties that will perk up a skin dulled by age or illness.

- **INVERT YOURSELF!** Lie face up on your bed with your head hanging down off the side to give a boost to the blood supply to your face. While yogis do headstands for hours, you'll only need a few minutes. And get up slowly, so you don't get dizzy.

- **REMEMBER THE POWER OF MAKEUP.** The next chapters will show you how to use artifice to help create beautiful, vital glowing skin.

AGER #4: RISKY BUSINESS

Sometimes I feel like calling in the Beauty Police (or at least bringing back Prohibition), for there are habits that lead to self-inflicted signs of aging, the worst sort, because they're preventable.

- **STOP SMOKING.** Cigarettes harm more than your lungs. You lose 25 mg of Vitamin C with each cigarette you smoke, and since C is a collagen booster, you don't have to be a math wizard to figure out that less C means more and earlier crows feet. Plus, smokers naturally tend to crinkle their eyes to avoid the smoke. And the physical act of smoking (lighting up, inhaling and exhaling) causes premature wrinkle lines around the mouth. So if health reasons don't force you to stop, maybe vanity will.

- **CURB DRINKING.** Too much alcohol causes dilation of the blood vessels, which leads to broken vessels . . . even to a spidery red nose if you have a serious problem (in which case you'll need a dermatologist).

  Alcohol also causes wrinkles because it dehydrates your skin, leading to—you guessed it—water loss. An occasional drink is OK; just don't overdo.

◆ **CONTROL YO-YO DIETING.** When you're on the merry-go-round of losing weight fast and regaining over and over, here's what happens to your face: During a weight gain, your skin has to stretch to cover the added fat; during the loss cycle, the skin sags and creases because the fat isn't there to shore it up. If you take the weight off slowly and keep it off, your skin will fit your face and body better, and your face won't look deprived of the water weight that is the first to go due to up-and-down dieting.

◆ **AVOID STRESS.** Hah! Unless you live in a cocoon, or have a meditation secret I certainly don't know about, you can't possibly follow this rule. The result: tension shows in your face, anger can show up as red blotches on your face and throat. The prescription: Take one B-complex vitamin daily along with your multiple. The Bs are doubly skin aiding: The components work to calm your nerves, which may help soothe those angry red tension breakouts, and they help nourish red blood cells.

◆ **AVOID THE SUN.** As I mentioned, "Ol Sol's" rays destroy collagen, which is why the phrase "healthy tan" is an oxymoron. Make no mistake, sitting in your swimsuit by the beach or pool is more dangerous than bungee jumping when it comes to reckless treatment of the skin. The sun gives your skin the look and feel of aged leather—fine for a handbag, but it will make you look like an old bag. If you check skin that is not regularly exposed to the sun (under your breasts, inside your forearm), you'll see how your protected skin can look. Quite a difference. In fact, some doctors now believe that 90% of what we recognize as signs of aging (wrinkling, leathery consistency) is due to sun exposure.

Use a sunscreen with an SPF of at least 15, and reapply often when you must go out in the sun. Consider using a moisturizer or foundation containing a sunscreen, too. The nose, earlobes, lips and cheekbones get greatest exposure; cover with a sunscreen and then lather on a zinc oxide sunblock.

If your skin is sunburned (this is the last time, right?), chapped or otherwise irritated, splash with cool water and skip the towel dry; it will hurt. Instead, set your blow drier on cool, hold it six inches from your face and you'll dry without that irritating rubbing.

Ozone effects. Whether or not you believe that there's a hole in the ozone layer allowing more harmful sun rays to reach us, many scientists do. So even if you don't live in the southern or western states, err on the side of caution and keep a sunscreen with you when you venture outdoors.

Skiing and the sun. Sun reflects as harshly off of snow as it does off of sand, so you must wear a sunscreen when you ski, even if the thermometer is chilly enough to cause the marshmallows to freeze in your hot cocoa!

AGER #5: BREAKOUTS AND BLEMISHES

If clear, glowing skin equals youth and health, skin that is losing its elasticity and starting to wrinkle is made worse when burdened with blackheads and other skin imperfections. Let's see what we can do about them.

SOLUTIONS

- **BANISH BLACKHEADS.** Did you know a blackhead has nothing to do with dirt? It's really a plug of hardened oil trapped within a pore. When the surface of the plug meets the air, it turns black. To dislodge the oil plug, which sometimes seems as tough as getting an oil well to gush forth, try the following:

  Apply hot (not scalding) towels to your skin for five minutes (it's the same principle barbers use before giving a shave in a barber shop); heat softens everything.

- **STEAM OPENS YOUR PORES.** Put two to three tablespoons of your favorite herbs or teas into a pot of boiling water. The herbs scent the water, making inhaling a pleasant experience. Remove pot from the stove and cover both your head and the pot with a towel to lock in the steam. Keep your head tented for about ten minutes while sitting (standing, you may get dizzy and you don't want to fall face first into superhot water!). Alternative: If you have the *Adrien Arpel Thermal Steamer*, follow the pore-opening directions.

- **EXTRACT.** Your oil plugs are now softened, so you're ready for do-it-yourself blackhead removal. Should you or shouldn't you? The experts say no, leave it to the professionals. But I'm a realist, and I know you're probably going to try, so here's how: wrap a soft, unscented facial tissue around your index fingers, dip in alcohol to disinfect and squeeze gently with your fingertips. If the plug is ready, it will lift out easily. But if your skin is becoming reddened and little crescent nail impressions are forming as you squeeze, the stubborn blackhead wants to remain *in situ*; leave it for another time or a professional set of fingers.

◆   **USE A COMMERCIAL PEELING AGENT.** These non-chemical peelers contain waxes, vegetable products and other ingredients that help de-clog by gently rolling away the dry, dead skin that's covering the pore opening.

◆   **MAKE YOUR OWN BLEMISH LOTION.** Don't use teenage acne and blemish fighters if you're over twenty-five. They're too strong for skin that is starting to wrinkle and/or lose elasticity. Instead, add a pinch of alum to two ounces of witch hazel or your astringent.

- ◆   Alternate lotion: Add 1/4 teaspoon boric acid to eight ounces of your astringent or witch hazel.
- ◆   No witch hazel? Calamine lotion strategically placed is a good overnight blemish fighter (so is milk of magnesia). After the calamine (or milk of magnesia) dries, apply your night creme and the calamine will keep your creme off of the trouble spot.
- ◆   If you find a blemish lotion you like, don't slather it all over your face. Apply only to affected areas with a Q-Tip.
- ◆   If one small pimple just won't go away before a big night out, cover it with brown or black eyebrow pencil and turn it into a beauty mark.
- ◆   If you have pimples on your back and you're planning to wear a low-cut dress, apply a styptic pencil (the gizmo you use when you nick yourself shaving) a few times a day to supercharge the drying process.

◆   **TO COMBAT OILY, MESSY SKIN.** Use a commercial mud mask or make your own. Mix fuller's earth or kaolin (available in drug stores) with water until you have a peanut butter-like paste. Spread it on your damp face and leave on three minutes. Remove with cool, wet washcloth.

- ◆   Consider a nose mask if your nose turns so oily your shine breaks through makeup almost as fast as you leave your bathroom mirror. Combine 1/2 teaspoon USP fine grind pumice, 1/4 teaspoon alum and enough witch hazel to make a paste. Spread on nose, leave for three minutes, rinse with cool water and apply makeup as usual.

Tip: If any paste or creme you formulate yourself is too runny, you can always add a little talcum powder or powdered milk as a thickening agent.

- **SKIP THE SOAP.** The alkaline ingredient (usually salt) which gives soap its cleansing quality is also very drying. That's why after you wash with soap, your skin may feel so tight you can barely crack a smile. Use a non-soap cleansing gel, foam, or nature-based cleansing grains instead. Whatever you use, rinse well to avoid leaving any residue behind.

- **PILLOW TALK.** I hate to increase your laundry level, but if you are experiencing skin breakouts, and using creme or overnight pimple fighters, you need to change your pillow case nightly. You wouldn't walk around all day with your face touching a soiled, polluted cloth, would you? Don't give your skin night terrors.

- **NIGHT SWEATS.** If you find your face literally sweating under your night creme, you need to change to a formula with less wax. The "waxy buildup" may be sealing your skin too effectively, causing your trapped sweat glands to become overactive, producing overnight breakout.

FRESHENER FACTS

- You can set dry skin tingling without robbing it of moisture by combining 3/4 ounces each of strained lemon and lime juice. Shake, refrigerate and swab over face with cotton balls.

- If you'd prefer an even gentler freshener, combine equal parts rosewater and milk, refrigerate and use as above.

- If your astringent/freshener/toner seems too drying for your skin, wet your cotton ball with water, then put your astringent on it. The water will cut the astringent's power.

- If your out of freshener, check your cupboard for apple cider vinegar. Dilute the "ACV", with twice as much water (kind of like a fat-free salad dressing!) and wipe over damp face with a cotton ball.

MASKED MARVELS

Of course! I'm a great believer in facial masks. There is nothing more luxuriating and skin/psyche reviving than putting your complexion in the hands of a professional facialist. But if you have neither the time nor the money for a salon facial, the following at-home masks, which you can make quickly and apply with either your fingers or your skin machine, will help give your face the look and feel of soft, supple radiant skin.

Note: Always apply your chosen formula to damp skin. Lie down for 10 minutes, put your feet up and relax while Nature takes its course. Rinse thoroughly using a washcloth or your cupped palms . . . and tepid water.

SIMPLE DRY SKIN DETERRENT MASKS

- **THE MENOPAUSE MASK,** for skin that has been around the block a few times. Soften honey in the top half of a double-boiler. Prick open and add the contents of two Vitamin A capsules, and two Vitamin E capsules. Stir in a package of brewer's yeast. Paint on face and throat with a pastry brush.

- **MOISTURIZE WITH AVOCADO.** Just remove skin, mash the pulp with a fork and apply to face. The oil in the avocado works wonders; enrich it with the contents of a Vitamin A capsule if you're feeling ambitious.

- **HOLD THE MAYO.** Mayonnaise makes a great skin soother (its oil, egg yolk and vinegar are skin-enhancing ingredients). Slather on face with upward strokes. Increase its power by mixing in an extra yolk (you don't have to worry about cholesterol when applying externally!)

- **MILK AND HONEY.** Soften honey by warming it slightly. Combine with powdered milk and apply to face.

- **BARBER SHOP TRICK.** Heat a few tablespoons of petroleum jelly in the top of a double boiler till just warm. Apply to damp skin. Cover face with a towel soaked in warm water for fifteen minutes to soften skin (though your routine won't be followed by a shave and haircut).

- **ALL-TOGETHER GOOD.** Combine one tablespoon glycerine, one egg yolk, two tablespoons heavy cream and two teaspoons of honey. Add powdered milk to make a paste, and apply with fingertips.

- **VITAMIN E EXPERIENCE.** Prick open two capsules and add to two tablespoons of yogurt for a softening treatment.

- **OLIVE OIL** is a great skin conditioner. Warm slightly, apply a thin coat. When ready to remove, blot off with freshener, then rinse.

SIMPLE OILY SKIN MASKS

- **MASK POMODORO.** Tomatoes are very acidic, making them good for the acid mantle and effective oil blotters. Combine crushed, skinned pulp with enough powdered milk or talc to make a paste and spread over oily areas of face.

- **YOGURT YUMMY.** Mix 1/2 cup vanilla yogurt, 1 teaspoon lemon juice, two teaspoons grapefruit juice and a dash of peppermint extract.

- **MASH NOTE.** Mash together 1/2 banana and six strawberries. Smooth over face (unless you're allergic to the berries).

- **TAKE "C" AND SEE.** Mix one teaspoon of liquid Vitamin C into four ounces of yogurt or sour cream. "C" is ascorbic acid, a good skin astringent.

BEFORE YOU GO OUT SKIN REVIVERS

- **TEMPORARY TIGHTENER.** Take two egg whites, beat till firm. Apply to damp face with fingertips or artist's paint brush and let harden. Rinse with cool water and notice your skin has a tight, firm feeling and the pores look smaller.

  Note: Nothing can really close enlarged pores, but different cosmetics and treatments can give pores the appearance of shrinking (by slightly irritating and swelling the surrounding skin) and that's just as good.

- **PORE MINIMIZER.** Combine two ounces each of witch hazel, white cooking wine (the jug variety; no need to use the expensive stuff), rosewater and camomile tea. Toss in a dash of oil of peppermint and refrigerate. Shake before using, and apply with cotton ball for a nice skin wake-up call.

- **FACE BRACER.** When you take out your WaterPik to brush your teeth, turn the nozzle on your face to get your circulation going. Just make sure you avoid your eyes.

- **ARCTIC BLAST.** Wrap an ice cube in a handkerchief and stroke across face before you put on MakeUp. After you make-up, *pat* ice over face to set MakeUp. Ice Additives: Splash freshly squeezed lemon or lime juice into water as you're setting ice cubes for an additional face tingle.

NOW, VOYAGER: TRAVEL TIPS

- A five hour plane trip can be as drying as a sprint across the Sahara. The moisture robbers: cabin compression and air conditioning. There's no tent to slip into, but you can create a face oasis by drinking plenty of water (eight ounces per hour) and patting H_2O on your face in-flight (keep a small plastic bottle and some cosmetics squares handy).

- My assistant uses those little black 35mm throwaway film cannisters for everything when she travels: aspirins, sewing kit, hand cremes, shampoo.

- If you're afraid your precious potions will spill en route, melt equal parts candle wax and petroleum jelly, swish around the openings of bottles and jars and let dry.

- Forgot your skin exfoliator? Swipe a couple of sugar packets from the restaurant stash, mix a small amount with a dab of cold creme and voila, slougher!

Chapter Two
Gorgeous Hair
and How To Get It

What's one of the first things you notice about young girls (you, not your husband)? For me, it's that shining curtain of thick, luxe hair trailing down their backs . . . hair that turns every toss of the head into a seduction.

Now, most of us no longer have the time, energy, or hair texture to devote to that high-maintenance, siren look, so we'll reserve the to-the-waist hair for the teenagers.

But post-pubescent locks needn't reveal your age. Whether you wear your crowning glory grazing your shoulders or cropped close to your head, hair is one of the easiest things about yourself you can change. It may take months to lose ten pounds, but in a couple of hours you can make yourself look dramatically younger, different, even happier with a change of hairstyle.

The quick turn around a new hair look provides doesn't, alas, mean having great-looking tresses is a completely work-free proposition; neither should hair be the focus of your day. Some swift routines, and professional know-how, can help restore and keep the shine, gloss and swingability of younger-looking hair.

So if your hair looks like the stuffing from an old pillow, and dishwater is more vibrant than the color you now have, you needn't walk around with tresses that make you look like a reject from "Night of the Living Dead". Hair should be the part of your look you change most frequently.

After all, what other part of your body can you cut and it obligingly grows back. Or, you paint it orange, then color it brunette. So have fun, it's only hair . . . but wait till you see what you can do with it, and what it can do for you.

Why am I an expert on hair, you may well be asking? For over 25 years of my career, *Arpel* had been affiliated with in-store beauty salons in major department stores all over the U.S. and Canada. We regularly did combination hair and skin makeovers together. So I've been able to pick brains (if not, the scalps) of the top hair professionals in the country to bring you the newest hair revitalizing information. Here goes:

BIO BACKGROUND

You needn't be a biochemist to turn blah hair terrific, but a few facts about your tresses will help you understand why you have to treat hair a certain way.

The hair you see on your head is dead, a dead protein called *keratin*. The only living part of the hair (the root system consisting of hair follicles, oil producing glands, blood supply) lies beneath the scalp, and that's where growth and nourishment take place. Mom Nature was smart, because no matter how we abuse our hair up top—a bad dye job, too many chemicals, heavy handed use of the blow dryer— new replacement hair will come up healthy.

To impress the scientists in your family, throw around the words *cuticle, cortex* and *medulla* . . . the components of the hair shaft. Since the experts still disagree about the medulla's function (and fine-haired people probably don't even have one), we'll concentrate on the "C & C" hair factory.

Put a hair strand under a microscope and you'll see the outer layer, or cuticle, is actually made up of overlapping scales. When heat, hair color, perming or other treatments are applied, the scales lift and open, allowing the "damage" to seep into the cortex, the layer responsible for pigment and elasticity. Your goal will be to have the flattest cuticle in town, because when the scales lie smooth and therefore are as impenetrable as possible, your hair shaft will be healthy. Equally as important: Light reflects much stronger off of a smooth, flat surface than a ragged one, so if you want shiny hair you need a "closed cuticle".

DOWN FOR THE COUNT

How much hair is normal? It depends on the number of follicles: each follicle produces one strand. The average is about 90,000 follicles/hairs per redhead, 110,000 per brunette, and a whopping 140,000 per blonde. I don't know if blondes have more fun, but they have more hair because their individual hairs are thinnest, so more is necessary to insure good coverage.

Losing 50–100 hairs a day is standard operating procedure, no cause for alarm, because your hair factory is non-union; it works twenty-four hours a day, 365 days a year. New hair grows at the rate of 1/2" a month; it grows faster in summer than in winter, faster on younger women than older.

The ages between fifteen and thirty are prime time for long hair production. I hate to say you're over the hill at 31, but if you want waist-length hair, your time is running out. In fact, for most women 10" seems to be the limit for healthy hair, no matter how much we coddle. And, after a certain age, below shoulder length hair is aging. That's why old witches and hags in fiction are always shown with long, scraggly locks—it's a look that works for them, not for us!

THINNING HAIR

SCALP STATE. Look to your scalp—or beneath it—for clues to thinning hair. The capillaries in the papilla (part of the hair follicle) bring nourishment to the hair via the blood. If your scalp is scaly due to seborrhea (inflamed hair particles that mimic dandruff), patches of psoriasis or other pasties, hair growth (and/or lustre) could be adversely affected.

Why? Let's detour back to biology class. Hair, like skin, contains sebaceous glands. The sebum is the oil that gives your hair shine. If the glands are overactive, the shine turns to oil; glands underactive or blocked by a scalp condition like those mentioned above give you dry hair, or worse hair that can't fight its way topside through the debris clinging to the scalp.

Note: What you put on your hair or do to it can cause perfectly healthy hair to look dry or oily, but that's a beauty condition. If you think your scalp difficulties indicate more than ordinary dandruff, that's a health condition, see a dermatologist. Otherwise, stick with me.

HORMONES. If your hair is looking thinner as you're getting older, blame it on your hormones, which may no longer be raging. As estrogen production slows down, the male hormone androgen (which we all possess) has more room to cause trouble—i.e., some that falls out may not grow back. But take heart. True male pattern baldness is extremely rare in women, and with a little sleight of hand (and a well-stocked beauty shelf) you can pump up the volume and make thinning locks look thicker.

MEDICAL MAYHEM. Hormones aren't the only culprit. If you've been ill or suffered other bodily trauma, hair loss may follow. Certain medications, thyroid deficiencies, anemia can also put your hair factory on temporary strike. Check with your doctor; ditto if you are pregnant or, conversely, taking birth control pills. Whether your baby-making prowess is in full gear or in a chemically-induced holding pattern, you may notice some hair loss, but your tresses will fill out after the blessed event (or when you stop taking the Pill).

SHINE ON:
NEW LIFE FOR FADING, DULL HAIR

While I'm no magician, neither can Siegfried and Roy give you back your "sweet sixteen" hair (and the firm body that went with it . . . I should know; I can't even *remember* my sixteenth birthday!). But attractive hair with vibrance and bounce, that I can do—from the inside out. Because what I tell you to put on your hair is the icing; what you put in your body is the cake. So, batter up.

ALPHABET SOUP:

Vitamins play an important part in hair health.

* Ingest the B-complex vites for primo hair as well as super skin. By strengthening the hair shaft, Bs contribute to good-looking growth. They also counteract the stress (they're called Nature's tranquilizer) that can lead to a tight scalp, and poor circulation. By the way, overindulgence in alcohol destroys Bs.

* Remember Vitamin C, 500 mg in the morning, another 500 mg at night. If I couldn't convince you to take C for your skin, do it for your hair. C rebuilds tissues, and helps detox the blood that carries nutrients to the scalp. Smoking destroys Cs.

* Take E and see. Start with 100 IU a day, work up to 400. E is a healer, promotes shine, but you have to skip it if you have high blood pressure or other circulatory problems.

OTHER INTERNAL BOOSTERS:

* Mineral mix. Make sure your multivite/multimineral supplement contains zinc (strengthens hair), copper (fights greying), and iron (if you test anemic).

- Eat protein (after all, that's what hair is made of): chicken, turkey, fish, lowfat cheeses, etc.

- Add one tablespoon of oil to your daily diet if you want glossy hair. A completely no-fat diet is a no-no for hair health.

LOOSEN UP . . .

Tension's by-product, a tight scalp, means constricted blood vessels, and the narrower the vessels, the fewer the nutrients flowing to the papillae where new hair is born. Here's a stimulating scalp massage.

- Make a simple massage oil to help your fingers slide over your scalp easier. Warm 1/4 cup olive oil; add the contents of two capsules of Vitamin E. Stir.

- Brush and de-tangle your hair.

- Sit down. Drop head forward and rotate three times in a circle.

- Rub palms and fingers together briskly to warm them.

- Starting at nape of neck, reach tented fingers under hair and manipulate scalp in short, circular motions, using fingertips, not nails.

- Work up along scalp, doing sides of head.

- Lift head and shift fingertips to front hairline and manipulate crown with circular motions.

- When entire scalp moves easily beneath your fingertips, massage the back of your neck and radiate outward to your shoulders.

- Relax for five minutes, then shampoo.

THE PRO HOW TOS

Sure, you've been washing your hair since kindergarten, but that doesn't mean your technique is correct. Here,

- If you have sensitive or allergy-prone eyes, put a layer of petroleum jelly above your brows and around your hairline to keep shampoo and treatment products from dribbling down into your eyes and stinging.

- Always gently brush hair first to dislodge any loose debris, and distribute oils away from the scalp and along the hair shaft.

To brush, bend your head forward, start at the nape and brush outward to the ends. But forget grandma's 100 strokes a day advice. She may have been right about chicken soup, but she's wrong on this: All that tugging is too harsh on the scalp and hair.

- If your hair is normal to dry, run your head under the faucet for sixty seconds. Don't plop shampoo directly from the bottle onto your head. If you're in the shower, you can't see what you're doing and you'll probably use too much ... and most of it will be concentrated in one place. Apply one teaspoon of shampoo to your palm, mix it with a lot of water to get some lather going, and distribute through hair with palm and fingertips. Massage gently into hair and scalp to clean.

- If your hair is oily, apply the shampoo to your palm as above, then put on dry hair and massage in *before* you even turn on the faucet. The theory: Oil and water don't mix, so you'll get the cleansing agents directly where they're needed, without H_2O interfering. Now add your water, a little more shampoo if necessary, and massage gently with your fingertips to cleanse.

- Oily hair oddity. You'd think the oilier your hair, the more frequently you should wash? Well, you think wrong. Too much washing with too much shampoo can actually dry out your hair and scalp, causing your internal hair factory to produce more oil to compensate. Cut down on the shampoo.

- The everyday myth. There's no rule written in cold creme that says "Thou shalt shampoo daily." It could be your hair stays clean, fresh and manageable for a couple of days. When you do shampoo, the Second Commandment is not "Thou shalt lather twice." The less shampoo you use, the less you leave behind to coat and dull your hair. If you don't get the copious foam quality you like with one sudsing, add more water, not more shampoo. If you just can't help yourself, you find yourself lathering twice, here's cold turkey for shampoo addicts: Add some water to your shampoo bottle (up to 1/2 the contents) before you even get in the shower. Shake before each use. You'll trick yourself into using less shampoo, save money and find rinsing goes a whole lot faster.

- Concentrate on cleaning the scalp (from whence oil comes) and the top third of hair near the roots. Devote less time to the middle and ends of your hair: Scalp oils usually can't get that far if you wash frequently, so the older "end" hair stays cleaner. In any case, three minutes of gentle shampooing is enough unless you've just emerged from a coal mine.

◆ If your scalp is naturally oily but your hair has dried due to age or injudicious use of heat and processing, wet your hair, then coat the bottom third with conditioner before you shampoo. Now, you can use a cleanser and wash the scalp area without further drying the hair shafts.

◆ If your shampoo is coming on too strong (you know the feeling— it cleans so well you can't do anything with your hair because too much oil has been stripped away), try diluting two parts water to one part product. Still don't like it? Use it to clean your brushes and combs.

◆ You absolutely adore "Madame Zimza's Artichoke Shampoo" and want to chuck everything else from your shower shelf? Sorry. You need to find a few shampoos you like, and alternate their use. Hair gets bored easily, and stops responding to certain formulas. Rotate products, and you get new additives, so your hair stays happy.

PACK IT IN

Conditioning hot oil treatments, the kind you leave on for ten to thirty minutes, are great for dry, damaged hair. But even if you can manage just 5 minutes, you'll give your hair a boost. Of course, you don't want to spend 30 minutes in the shower, twiddling your thumbs and crooning Elvis' greatest hits while your conditioner takes. Here's how to open up your schedule for a tress treat:

◆ In the summer, slather on a hot oil treatment before you work in the garden or head for the beach. Or, if you're planning to swim, make this waterproof conditioner pack:

Whisk together two tablespoons apple cider vinegar, one tablespoon glycerine, one tablespoon hot olive oil, one tablespoon coconut oil, and two eggs. Comb through your hair before you take the plunge, or after you get home and shower off the sea salt and chlorine. Leave on thirty minutes if possible.

◆ If you go to a gym, comb through your conditioner, then cover-up with an old baseball cap. You're heading for the showers anyway.

If you jog, condition before you run. You use a treadmill at home? Perfect time to condition.

- You're planning a relaxing aromatherapy bath? Cap your head with conditioner while you're in the tub.

KITCHEN CONDITIONERS

Here are some fun ways to raid the fridge and cupboard for hair nourishers and shiners. Apply any of the following to just-shampooed wet hair, leave in five minutes, rinse well with warm, then cold, water.

- Peel and smash an avocado. Mix in one tablespoon of wheat germ oil.

- Add one tablespoon Vitamin E oil to 3 tablespoons of mayonnaise.

- Stir one egg yolk into 1/2 cup yogurt.

- Beat two whole eggs, 1/4 cup cooking sherry, 1/2 cup water.

- Combine 1/2 cup safflower oil and 1/2 cup honey. Heat until they melt together. Make sure it's warm, not hot and apply to hair with one inch paintbrush.

RINSE CYCLE

Rinsing is the most important step in hair treatment: while what you put in your hair is crucial, taking it all off is more so. Unless you're using a stay-in product, after the shampoo and conditioner has done it's job, you must remove all traces or you'll have a dull, itchy residue that will coat your hair, disguising its natural shine.

The key ingredient, of course, is water. Rinse until you feel you've gotten all the residue out, then rinse for three minutes more. Make your final rinse in cold water, to close the cuticle, thus upping your hair's shine potential.

Have a little more time to spend? Brew up these do-it-yourself cuticle closers, and shine-on:

- For dark hair, mix one part apple cider vinegar to four parts water, and add 5 drops of peppermint oil. Blondes, substitute lemon juice for vinegar and skip the peppermint. Pour over hair as a final rinse and leave in.

- To add color as well as shine to natural hair:
  - ☺ Brunettes: Add one tablespoon rosemary, one tablespoon sage to two cups boiling water. Let steep 10 minutes. Strain, cool completely, refrigerate and pour over head, catching remains in shatterproof bowl, and reapplying till there's nothing left. Alternate: one cup espresso.
  - ☺ Blondes: Add one tablespoon camomile, one tablespoon marigold, one tablespoon orange peel and proceed as above.
  - ☺ Redheads: Combine one cup cranberry juice or beet juice with one cup water, proceed as above. Alternate: Red Zinger tea.

SPECIAL ADVANTAGES

DANDRUFF. It's itchy, flaky and definitely unsightly, but dandruff can be curbed before you're awash in a sea of white flakes. Some experts believe stress exacerbates the condition; for some people, it's worse in winter than in summer. Whatever the causes, there are two main types. Oily dandruff occurs when the sebum sacks attached to the hair follicle work overtime, causing the cells to clump together in greasy patches that eventually flake off as dandruff.

Dry dandruff means your scalp isn't producing enough oil or plain old moisture, so the cells have nothing to hold on to, and fall off in flakes.

Here, some helpful treatments for either variety. Their purpose is to cleanse the scalp and restore its proper moisture balance. Apply the following directly to the scalp; hair itself has nothing to do with dandruff.

P.S. If you haven't been rinsing your hair thoroughly, your dandruff could really be the result of shampoo or hairspray residue mimicking dandruffian flakes!

- Always begin with a scalp massage (see page 17–18) to loosen any debris before you treat. But skip the oil application, and give your hair (i.e., scalp) a few extra brushstrokes to rev up the circulation.

- Saturate a cotton ball with witch hazel, part hair into sections so you get good scalp coverage and apply to part lines. Leave on fifteen minutes. Rinse and shampoo.

- Mix an antiseptic like *Sea Breeze* skin lotion or clear/yellow mouthwash with an equal amount of water and apply to part lines as explained above.

- Combine one tablespoon each of Epsom salts, sea salts and baking soda and stir into four ounces mineral water.

- If you think your scalp flaking is due to dryness, apply two ounces of corn or coconut oil, 1/2 ounce apple cider vinegar and one tablespoon wheat germ oil to parted, sectioned hair.

- A teaspoon of your favorite cologne will help mask the smell when added to any of the above.

If none of these remedies banishes the flakes, check out the commercial shampoos labeled for dandruff control. They usually contain remedies like tar, sulfur, zinc, selenium pyrithione. They are harsher than regular shampoos, and may not be safe for color-treated hair. Read the labels carefully.

If you still get no relief, make an appointment with a dermatologist. You may have a more serious scalp disorder—seborrheic dermatitis or psoraisis are two that come to mind—and you may need prescription remedies.

- Final caveat: Don't perm or tint hair that's in the midst of a serious dandruff problem; your scalp is undergoing enough trauma without subjecting it to chemical processing.

STATIC ELECTRICITY. While not in the category of dandruff, this nuisance can make your hair look a fly-away mess, but it's easy to correct.

- Spray your hairbrush with a light mist of hairspray, then brush gently over already-styled hair.

- Put a dab of fabric softener diluted with water in your palm, rub gently over hair.

- Polish your hair after brushing. If you have my *Frizz Fixx*, place a few drops in the palm of your hand and apply lightly over entire head to create a supershine. Or, put 1/2 teaspoon of hand creme in your palm, rub palms together and lightly coat hair. Now, "polish" hair by tying a piece of silk around your hand and stroking your silk mitt over your hair.

FOLLICLE FOOLER STYLING GUIDE

They said it couldn't be done, but you've now gotten your hair into A-One condition: clean, shiny, swingy. Only problem is: You hate it!

If you feel your hair does nothing for your face, it's time for a new style. And, if it's been awhile since they checked your ID when you order a Bloody Mary, don't cry bloody murder. Use hair as camouflage, and style your way to a younger look.

Of course the cut is the basis from whence all good-looking hair comes. Get yourself to the best stylist you can afford, and don't forget to be as explicit as possible regarding what you're trying to accomplish. You and your stylist are a team. You're the coach, give him/her pointers . . . and then let him run with the ball (or should I say shears).

CHOOSE A HAIRSTYLE YOU CAN LIVE WITH

* Don't fight your hair texture. If your hair is curly, don't try to go straight, and vice versa. Unless you go for a perm, you'll be fighting a losing hair battle. You'll need too many products, too much time and too much heat.

    Texture and natural curl—how your hair looks and feels after you wash it, let it air dry and just run a comb through it—are pre-determined (has to do with the way the strand emerges from the follicle) and that is a matter of genetics. So blame your parents if you have a bush that would only make a "Chia Pet" happy. Go for a layered cut if you have curly hair, a blunt cut if your hair is straight.

* Do consider your lifestyle. If you're a working woman, a flowing mane of unkempt hair will add nothing to your image. You lead a more casual lifestyle? A severe short cap might not go with your sweats and jeans. We've come a long way, baby, but our hair still sends out messages. Make sure your head coordinates with your clothing. And, make sure you tell your stylists how you usually dress, since the first time he sees you, you may be sitting in his chair covered chin-to-knees with a plastic apron. Also tell your stylist the truth about how much time you spend on your hair every morning. No use pretending you're going to blow your hair for 1/2 hour when you run out of the house with your hair wet after a quick comb-through.

* Remember your two body types—tresses and torsos. If your hair has little body (it's fine), go with the all-one-length blunt cut to build in fullness, and try our *Hair Thickener*—it creates instant body. If you have lots of body (thick texture or curls), go with

layers that will help disguise the fact that your hair pretty much does what it pleases.

Your second type is your shoulders-to-ankles body. If you are narrow up top and wider at the hips, you need some length and fullness in your hairstyle to balance your torso shape.

- If your forehead is starting to line, consider bangs. They're perfect camouflage. If you wear full bangs like me, here's a good way to keep them sleek looking: Brush your wet bangs off of your forehead as you blow-dry. Now, brush bangs forward and dry from the top. They'll lie flat and straight. You may not want full bangs; wisps are effective at disguising your forehead, and they work well to minimize a receding hairline (for some women it's part of the aging process).

- If you want a quick shift, change your part. It can give a whole new look to your face shape. Moving your part around is also good for your hair, especially if it's thinning.

- If your crow's feet seem to be radiating out to the sides of your face, frame your face in soft waves and add some height to the crown to detract attention from crinkling eye skin.

- Ditto on the full crown idea for a sagging jawline. Try a pageboy or soft waves that cover the jaw demarcation line. Check your style from a sideview mirror to see if the length is right.

- Take advantage of electricity. Plug-in drying and styling aids make going from wet to set a breeze, but you have to make sure you don't dry the life out of your hair. Think of your hair as a fine silk blouse. You wouldn't tug it, twist it, burn it, would you? Not unless your daddy is a silk manufacturer! Well, neither can a daddy or a sugar daddy replace damaged hair, so you must use your appliances correctly.

  You know the blow-drying drill: let your hair dry as much as possible before you turn on the power to avoid prolonged heat exposure which could lead to damage; hold dryer six inches from hair; don't use more than 1000 watts of power; move dryer around when styling so you don't singe any one section of hair; dry your hair in sections, starting from the back; if your hair is thick, do one layer at a time rather than expecting heat to penetrate from the top.

If you're using electric rollers, make sure you use end papers to protect the driest part of your hair as well as to promote neater curls. Unwind slowly and from the bottom to protect against breakage. Use a machine that produces mist to counteract the heat.

A curling iron can be the most lethal hair appliance; used incorrectly the wand can break off hair and singe the scalp in seconds. Make sure hair is completely dry before you start winding, follow directions carefully and buy a Teflon-coated wand so your hair will slip out easily.

♦ A chignon or headband—anything that pulls the hair severely off the face should be avoided by anyone over 30; it brings all the little lines into too sharp a focus.

SETTING LOTIONS AND POTIONS

There are many styling lotions available, from glazes, pomades and gels to sleek and hold your hair, setting lotions for a roller set, mousses to impart volume and hairspray to mist your style under control. Read the product directions to make sure the finisher you choose is designed to give the effect you want. And start by using half of the suggested dose: often a little dab really will do you, and you don't want to give your hair that coated-with-gunk look (unless that's the punk style you're after!)

If you're out of setting lotions, consider the following:

♦ Flavored gelatin. Plop on hair with fingers, then comb through. Take softened lemon for blondes; strawberry for redheads and brunettes.

♦ Flat beer. Pour some in a glass. Comb through damp hair with wide-tooth comb.

♦ Egg whites. Beat two until frothy, comb through damp hair.

THE PERMANENT OPTION

Remember when I said you shouldn't fight your hair's texture? Well, there is one exception: If you're willing to have a perm, you can thumb your nose at your straight-haired ancestors (and your follicles) and get a curly look. Perming won't involve much extra daily care, because once it's done the curl lasts for months. Just keep in mind:

- Unless your mother is still cutting your meat, don't aim for a mass of ringlets. Trying to look too young can make you look too old. Use your perm to create body, waves or soft curls. The biggest perm plus: even if you're all thumbs and hate fussing with your hair, you can maintain your curl level for the life of the perm.

- A perm can make fine, healthy hair look thicker. That's because the chemicals used in the processing are alkaline, so they open your cuticle slightly, making each hair look thicker. Of course, that means you must condition.

- If your hair is thinning as opposed to fine, skip a perm until you have the reason for your hair loss diagnosed.

- Spring for a salon perm. Just leaving the chemicals on an extra few minutes can lead to frizzy disasters that sometimes can only be remedied by cutting. If you're an inveterate do-it-yourself, and a pro perm would be a budget breaker, make sure you have everything ready before you begin, turn on your answering machine . . . and follow directions scrupulously. This is no time to improvise.

- Most important: whether you do it or they do it, don't wash your hair for at least 48 hours after your perm; your curls/waves/body need a couple of days to really "set".

- Keep shine in mind. Perms are anti-shine for two reasons: 1) The processing chemicals are alkaline, therefore drying. 2) Light reflects best off of a flat surface, and curls and waves are anything but flat. The result: permed hair often looks dry, dull. Do the following:

- Skip your daily shampoo. Oil on a permed head travels down the hair shaft at a much slower pace; it doesn't need an everyday sudsing.

- Don't brush your hair; you'll pull out the curl. Instead, use a hairpick to style and never brush a wet perm. You'll create a knotty mass of kinky tangles. Because you don't brush, you're not distributing scalp oils effectively (another dulling factor). Compensate by massaging your scalp regularly to get the oils moving.

- Use a 60-second perm-safe (check the label) instant conditioner every time you wash. Heavy conditioning packs are too much weight for your curls. And, your shampoo should be marked safe for perms, too. If in doubt, ask your stylist for product recommendations.

- Let permed hair dry naturally whenever possible. If you must wash and go, consider two drying aids: 1) a diffuser, which you attach to the nozzle of your blow drier, to enlarge the area being dried so heat doesn't concentrate in one small section or 2) a 150 watt infrared light bulb. Find either in beauty supply shops (check the Yellow Pages) or see if your hairdresser can order one for you.

- To perk up a perm, give your head a sauna. Turn your shower on full blast, close the bathroom door and when the steam is such that you can write your name on your bathroom mirror with your finger, it's time to enter the bathroom. Note: You stand in the bathroom, not in the shower, unless you want to meet a handsome doctor in your local burn unit. The humidity will help recurl a flagging perm.

- If you don't have time to engage in shower power, water is still a good pick-me-up. Keep some mineral water in a spritz bottle, and mist your head. Watch the curls revive.

- The color/perm timetable. I really think one of these processes is enough for any head, but if you insist on both, perm first, and wait at least 10 days between procedures.

- Add on shine by rubbing a dab of *Alberto VO5* or styling gel between palms and gloss—don't rub—over hair.

THE ARPEL HAIR COLOR GUIDE: "HELLO, GORGEOUS!"

You say you aren't satisfied with your looks? You say you're tired of looking blah? You say you don't like the grey hairs sprouting from (or completely covering) your scalp?

Well, *I say* you don't have to take it anymore! That little container of hair tint can be as magical as a genie in a bottle, granting you the wish of younger looking gorgeous hair, if you follow some simple rules, and understand a bit of coloring chemistry.

Let's get the "tech talk" over with quickly. There are three main types of coloring processes, and they're easily classified by how they affect the hair molecules, and how long the color lasts once it's applied to hair. The molecules in *temporary* tints can't pass from the cuticle into the cortex (where color changes take place); they merely coat the hair surface, and last only till your next shampoo. They're good if you want to add a little life to your natural color, not if you want to make dramatic changes. If you've never tinted before, temps are an easy way to get your feet (or hair) wet.

Semi-permanent colorants have smaller molecules than the temps, and they're slightly alkaline, so some of the molecules sneak into the cortex as the alkalinity lifts the cuticle. When you shampoo after your application, the cuticle closes somewhat, keeping some molecules trapped in the cortex. (I feel like I should be wearing a lab coat and holding a pointer, but if I don't explain, who will?) The result: Semi-permanent colors last from four to six shampoos. They contain no peroxide, so you can't bleach or make dramatic color differences, but if you're not too grey, or you just want a subtle change or some highlighting, give them a try. Another plus: "Semis" fade gradually, so you needn't be concerned with root re-touchups.

Permanent colorings, known in the trade as aniline derivative tints, are the superstars of the coloring biz. They're what I've been using for years, and what you'll use when you're ready for a haircolor change that won't go away until you cut your hair off. In *single process* permanent tinting, hydrogen peroxide (called the developer; sounds much nicer than bleach) is mixed with a tint color (called the base), which has tiny molecules. Together they penetrate the cortex in one step, and stay cortex-bound as oxidation takes place. You have the flexibility to go several shades lighter or darker (but should you—we'll discuss), or successfully cover grey. You'll have to retouch your roots as new hair grows in.

Double-process blonding (DPB) gives the most startling color changes, allowing you to go from dark brown to drop-dead platinum. "DPB" is also the most potentially damaging hair treatment. In process one, your hair is stripped of all its color via a brew of hydrogen peroxide and ammonia water. This stripping/bleaching also increases your hair's porosity, so it can absorb step two: the toner, or blonding agent. Because bleached hair is more porous (i.e., weaker), it breaks more easily, is much drier and needs intense coddling.

Retouching is a must with permanent coloring, whether you single or double-process, and it's something you'll have to deal with every three to six weeks, depending on how fast your hair grows and how different your chosen color is from the new growth sprouting from your scalp. Here are three tricks to lengthen the time between touch-ups.

+ Eliminate your part. But choosing a hairstyle that's tousled, with no definite part line, you eliminate the most obvious place where roots will show.

+ Invest in an instant root touch-up kit. You just color over your part line and near the scalp until it's time for your touch-up. Or, buy a soft eyebrow pencil in the color closest to your hair shade. Melt the tip with a match, and apply with a sponge or Q-tip to your roots.

Should you double process? I personally think it's too harsh a treatment, and by trying to go so far from the genetic coloring you were born with, you're probably not flattering yourself.

HIGHLIGHTING: THE SMART ALTERNATIVE

If I've scared you out of double-process blonding your whole head, but you do feel blondes are the chosen hair people, consider hair highlighting: Whether you're lightening subtle strands of broader sections of your hair, the double-processing chemicals don't touch your scalp, and most of your hair is left alone. The secret is the application: The individual strands to be colored are wrapped in aluminum foil, then bleached. A toner can be applied to custom blonde the streak. *The best part:* re-touching is needed only two or three times a year; root regrowth isn't really noticeable. *The bad part:* you can't streak if you have dark brown or black hair; the contrast will make the streaks look grey or white.

Well-placed highlights can do more than provide instant glam to your hair; they're also a styling aid.

+ Highlighting all around the face (works well with shorter hair) brightens a sallow complexion, and draws the eye away from fine lines and wrinkles.

+ That jowly look can be minimized by up-top highlighting, around the crown and temples.

+ Widen a long face by highlighting the sides of hair and brushing the hair back off of the face.

Now that you know *how*, the question is "Who?" Who should blonde your hair, you or the salon experts? Yes, I know the drugstore shelf is lined with excellent products (including streaking kits), but you should not attempt a double-process job yourself; the potential to harm or ruin your hair is too great. If you can afford it, have the professionals do a single process permanent color job, too, because hairdressers have a trained eye for color, and can mix shades as well as adjust timing to your current hair color and texture. If regular trips to a colorist would wreck havoc with your budget, try the single-process shampoo-in creme-based tints; they're not as drippy and difficult to maneuver.

Just make sure you patch test before you tint: an allergic reaction is *not* the reaction you're looking for! And strand test, too, to make sure you'll be getting the color you want. Follow package testing and application instructions to the letter. Note: If you have any kind of scalp problem, nobody should touch your hair. Flaking, scaling, bleeding, itching—whatever stress your scalp is currently enduring, you have to correct it before you color your hair.

You're looking for someone, even if it's your grandson, to say "Hello, gorgeous. . ." Now that you understand a bit of the chemistry, let's talk color, and what factors will influence your choice.

AGE. When choosing hair color, first consider your age. As you get older, your hair starts fading to white, and, surprisingly, so does your skin. Though not as obvious, your complexion loses the natural color of youth. That's why it's not a good idea to return to the exact shade of hair you had when you first started voting. Very dark hair against an aging face produces too harsh a contrast, a garish effect. Go one or two shades lighter, even if you're trying to cover grey. If you were a golden blonde in your glorious youth, consider more honey tones. And if you always starred as the "carrot" in those school nutrition plays, look to the auburn tones.

NATURAL COLORING. And I don't mean just hair color. If you're more than 1/3 grey, look to your skin tones and eye coloring to help you choose a shade. Sallow skins and brown eyes look brighter with a coppery red, auburn or toned-down blonde . . . ruddy complexions should skip the red shades, go with softer brown and ash blondes . . . olive skinned, dark-eyed beauties can run the gamut from light brown to rich chestnut with auburn highlights . . . blue eyes and fair skin can go blonder, but not yellow-bright.

UNDER 25. If you insist on bold color changes, now's the time to do them. Quirky plums, nail polish reds, onyx blacks and visible-from-100-feet-away blondes go best with unlined faces.

CARING FOR COLORED HAIR

Yes, Virginia, there is a set of rules to follow. But even jolly old Santa can't make you feel as good as you do when you have a head full of lustrous hair color in a shade that makes you feel even better than you look. To maintain:

- Wash and condition with products specifically formulated for color-treated hair (read the labels), or products recommended by your stylist.

- Skip your daily shampoo. Your hair is definitely drier after coloring, so there is less oil to remove. Lather once, not twice, when you do shampoo.

- Don't leave the shower without applying a 60-second instant color-fast conditioner. Your hair craves moisture; you also might consider a monthly hot olive oil treatment.

- Be careful how you brush your hair. Color treated hair is dry, weaker than natural hair, especially along the scalp line, around the front and sides of your head. To avoid head-on breakage, sit down and bend over from the waist, starting to brush from the nape outward. You'll distribute oil without breaking processed hair.

- Don't forget to patch and strand test before each application . . . and to cover your newly tinted hair with a hat or scarf whenever you're in the sun. The sun doesn't highlight chemically colored hair; it just turns it brassy.

WHO YA GONNA CALL? Not ghost-busters, but mistake busters. For questions concerning hair color how-tos, and how not-tos, the experts at Clairol and L'Oreal are more than willing to supply answers and advice: Their numbers:
Clairol: (800) 252-4765
L'Oreal: (800) 631-7358

GORGEOUS IN GREY. It's true, some women look fabulous in grey hair. If you have a relatively unlined face, and thick, healthy looking grey hair with nice broad streaks of white in the front, you may want to stay grey. Use the right shampoos and conditioners for silver hair, and throw away your cigarettes. The smoke can turn your hair an elegant shade of yellow.

If you're staying grey because you have limp, thin grey hair (you know, fine as opposed to thinning due to fallout) and you think color would harm it, you're doing your hair a disservice. Permanent coloring products swell the shaft open and layer their thickening chemicals inside before "resealing," so coloring fine, healthy hair can actually give it more body and volume.

THE MUSIC OF THE NIGHT

The most inexpensive way to dress up your look for evening is to dress up your hair. Here, a few ideas to get you going, and the places to go are your craft shop and favorite flea market.

♦ Buy an inexpensive fake flower, spray with floral scent and pin in hair.

♦ For the holidays, weave silver and gold tinsel through a braid or chignon. Or try the silver/gold cord used to wrap presents. Note: If the chignon looks too severe, pull forward wispy bangs, and a few strands around the sides of your face.

♦ Buy inexpensive costume jewelry—clip-on earrings work well; so do rings ornamenting a braid. Glass beads or tiny seed pearls wrapped around strands of hair are also pretty.

♦ Spritz a bit of hair spray over one section of your hair; dust on silver, gold, purple (your choice) glitter.

♦ Add some mystery by wearing a little black hat with a veil. Pair it with ruby red lipstick.

♦ Glue seashells or lace to plain tortoiseshell combs.

♦ Just remember one rule: Go for the elegant, not cute, when it comes to hair accessories. Leave pigtails for the gym, and forget those little plastic bunny/pony barrettes beloved by toddlers, unless you want to be mistaken for Bette Davis in "Whatever Happened to Baby Jane?"

CHAPTER THREE
MAKEUP & CAMOUFLAGE

Someone said (or should have) that "Beauty is an illusion". She or he must have been speaking about the art of making up. Probably what was really meant was that it doesn't hurt if you're one part magician when you're applying cosmetics. So, how can you become a MakeUp magician? It's really not that difficult. You do have to learn a few tricks about light and dark, highlighting and shading and you have to be very honest about your negative and positive features when you look in the mirror. Once you've done that, with my simple to follow instructions, it's *abracadabra and away we go.*

One advantage you have just because you're living in the 1990s is that this is an era of "anything goes"—there are *no* hard and fast rules about beauty. Individuality counts in the age of self-assured women. But do remember what we discussed in the first chapter. The better shape your skin is in, the better the finished MakeUp application will make you look. Unlike a snake, we can't shed our skin and move away from it—so we have to take care of what we have on a regular basis.

One question I've often been asked is "When should I wear MakeUp?" When you feel good, you want to wear MakeUp so that you look as great as you feel. MakeUp really perks you up when you're feeling down. When you're tired, MakeUp will help you look refreshed and, believe me, if you look refreshed, all of a sudden you'll find yourself feeling refreshed. If you're wan and pale, it helps you look healthy. And if you're too healthy and All-American looking and want to appear sexy or even a bit sultry, MakeUp can take care of you too. The nice part about MakeUp is you can wear it whenever you feel the need. But, you don't need, in fact mustn't, wear MakeUp when you're sleeping. Your skin needs the rest as much as you do.

A few more *caveats* before we actually start with your MakeUp lesson. Actually, you can slap-dash MakeUp on anywhere. But, to do a truly effective job—and my Mom always said whatever you do is worth doing right—you should establish your MakeUp location. Good lighting is essential; they say that natural light is the best. However I'm not so sure. After all, how much time do most of us spend in natural light? If you have a mirror with lights forming the frame, you're all set. If not, set up lights so that both your face *and* the mirror are illuminated. Experiment with light placement and wattage. A dimmer switch is a big bonus in helping you see yourself in all kinds of light—from romantic mood lighting to the harsh department store dressing room light bulbs. When you can see every line and blemish clearly, stop. You've got it right. A comfortable chair is also important. And, you'll need a flat surface so you can:

a) arrange all of your tools and products in sequence (a kitchen drawer flatwear separator tray on a lazy Susan is a great MakeUp organizer),

b) prop up your elbows for stability when using the various MakeUp brushes.

Speaking of brushes—you'll need more than one to become a MakeUp artist. Your *Basic Brush Wardrobe* should include Lip Brush, Eye Shadow Brush, Blush Brush and a Finishing (Powder) Brush. Once you're really skilled at applying your MakeUp, you might want to consider a *Brush Wardrobe for Experts*, which includes all of the brushes in the Basic Kit *plus* an EyeBrow "Brushing" Brush, an EyeBrow "Application" Brush, and an EyeLiner Brush. With the exception of a Brow Application Brush, which needs the firmness of a nylon bristle, natural bristle brushes work best. Be sure to clean your brushes regularly. Put your brushes in a solution of 1 Tablespoon automatic dishwashing powder with 8 oz. of warm water. Swirl the brushes around in this solution to loosen the debris. Then rinse in running water until the water runs clear. Drain the brushes by letting them stand overnight, bristle side up, in a cup or glass. Make sure they're completely dry before you use them again.

THE 10 BASIC STEPS IN 10 MINUTES
(. . . AFTER SOME PRACTICE)

1 — Moisturizing
2 — Applying UnderBase (or Skin Imperfection Coverup)
3 — Applying Foundation
4 — Camouflaging Line & Shape Imperfections
5 — Applying Blusher & Contouring*
6 — Creating EyeBrows
7 — Applying EyeShadows

8 — Brushing on Mascara*
9 — Making Lips*
10 — Setting Your MakeUp

*On a day when you absolutely cannot face the idea of spending ten minutes looking in the mirror, *at least* use the three asterisked procedures shown above and put on my Lazy Day Face—Lipstick, Blush and a little Lash Thickener and Mascara. The day you bump into your high school sweetheart, you'll thank me for encouraging you to leave your Naked Face in the bathroom.

MOISTURIZING — ALSO SEE CHAPTER 1

Once your face is completely cleansed, you're ready for your moisturizing lotion. (If you're even one hour over 18 years of age, you need a moisturizer. Don't skip it. Remember, Grandma Adrien is watching.) Again check Chapter One to find the moisturizing product that's best for you. Better yet, if you have a jar of the *Adrien Arpel Skin Correction Complex—Four Cremes In One*, you won't need anything else. The *Four in One*, with Alpha Hydroxy, is a day creme, a night creme, a moisturizer and a wrinkle creme. It's available separately or as part of my *Skin Correction Kit*. If you don't have it, just watch for it when I'm on television.

By the way, if you put on your moisturizer as you get out of the shower, while your face is still damp more water will be "sealed in". And while you're at it, don't forget to moisturize your throat.

Tip: Be sure you let the moisturizer settle a few moments before you proceed, to avoid diluting your UnderBase.

UNDERBASE
OR IT'S TIME TO CONSIDER CAMOUFLAGE

Incidentally, I discuss UnderBase and Camouflage products any time I appear on television or at department store seminars because I truly believe that no woman on Earth should be without them. Whether skin flaws are from the aging process or from a gene pool handed down from a great, great grandmother, the art of camouflage is as necessary to today's woman as it is to a General planning his battle strategy. It's not for nothing that MakeUp has been called "war paint".

We are in a war—a war against Father Time and Mother Nature. Fortunately, our cosmetic arsenal contains many weapons to combat the flaws and blemishes sent our way. Almost every cosmetic can be used to camouflage or improve something. However, the essentials are:

- concealers in stick form, available in a wide range of colors, and
- creme concealers sold in flesh tones, whites or pale, pale blues, greens and lavenders.

Light reflects well off these latter shades and when used on dark areas, makes them appear lighter which makes them great for "raccoon eyes" and other dark pigmented spots.

Tip: Remember to emphasize good points with light colors; de-emphasize negatives points with dark shades.

The basic purpose of an UnderBase is to correct or camouflage uneven or undesirable skin tones. The rule is: Use a tone one or two shades lighter than the tone of your Foundation. The creme concealers are best for camouflaging larger areas of skin. Stick concealers are better for dabbing onto smaller areas, such as under the eyes, on minor blemishes, and on small and shallow lines. But either one can do double-duty for the other if you already have either in your cosmetics collection. Just keep reading for more ideas and tips and then, practice, practice, practice. Blend into your skin; but don't blend too much. This is the only MakeUp step where it's possible to blend too much. You should still be able to see a trace of the CoverUp when you apply your Foundation. Another warning—don't have a heavy hand when using UnderBase or it will cake in crinkles, creases and those unlaughable laugh lines. Remember—less is better—don't overdo it.

CoverUps To Use
Before You Apply Your Foundation

UNDER-EYE SHADOWS OR CIRCLES

Dab your creme or stick concealer in a shade one tone lighter than your Foundation in three dots just below the bottom of the dark area. Blend gently—there is delicate tissue below the eyes. Pat, don't rub, upward and outward onto the dark circles. Should the darkness still be apparent, apply one of the pastel cremes (pale green, blue or lavender) first and then, blend the skin-toned concealer over the pastel layer. Do *not* use white because it will call attention to the area. Be sure you use a concealer that glides on. If your concealer drags or pulls at the delicate skin under your eyes, rub some on the palm of your hand and blend with a few drops of moisturizer. Apply mixture with your fingertips. An alternate solution is to use your *Adrien*

Arpel Opal Day Eye Gel or *Line Softener Stick*. If you don't have either of those, you could spread a minute amount of castor oil on the eye area and then cover up with your concealer stick.

Tip: Heavy Mascara on your lashes makes it look as if your own dark shadows are the shadows from lush lashes, rather than from lack of sleep or having at least one family of raccoons on your family tree. If you wear glasses which magnify your dark shadows, use a lighter colored Foundation in the eye area rather than a thicker layer of concealer.

TINY LINES AT LIPS

Run a concealer stick or pencil in shade similar to your Foundation lightly across the top of your upper lip line to fill in those tiny "paper" cuts. Blend until these tiny crevices are even with the surrounding skin. You can also use this concealer to balance any minor dark-toned areas at the corners of your mouth.

Tip: Don't be afraid to try different ways and different colors when you're concealing imperfections. However, I suggest you do your experimenting on a lazy afternoon—not just before an important dinner party or meeting.

BLEMISHES & BREAKOUTS

If you don't have any special products to deal with the occasional blemish, make your own. Mix one drop of camphor and three drops of Foundation; then, dab onto the affected spot. Or, mix a few drops of antiseptic with a few drops of your Foundation and cover the blemish. In both cases, let the mixture set before you continue with the rest of your MakeUp application.

Tip: Get an eye dropper at the drug store and keep it for such "emergencies".

NOSE TO MOUTH LINES & FROWN LINES

To make these lines less noticeable, dip a Q-Tip into baby oil and paint the lines carefully. Apply some lighter-than-your-Foundation concealer stick to tip of your index finger and stroke the concealer over the oiled lines. Blend completely. In cold weather, as an alternate to the oil, paint your lines with a flavorless chap-prevention stick and cover with your concealer. Blend to smoothness.

Tip: If your face is a bit puffy, making your lines look deeper than normal, use a pastel shade (pale blue, green or lavender) to cover up.

MINOR SCARS

Small cavity-like scars, such as those resulting from chicken pox or acne, are camouflaged by filling in the indentation with a concealer stick one or two shades lighter than your Foundation. Better yet, use the *Adrien Arpel Line Fill.* It may take several layers until the scar and surrounding skin are level; blend with the fingertips, a small brush or sponge.

RUDDY OR PALE/SALLOW SKIN TONES

Few of us are born with porcelain perfect skin tones. Fortunately skin that is too ruddy or too sallow can be camouflaged rather easily. In addition to selecting your Foundation colors carefully (more about that a little later), you'll need a color-correcting UnderBase. Any pale lavender creme CoverUp will work beautifully. If you're on a beauty budget and don't want to spend any of the allocation on a special effects covering product, you can use a lavender creme EyeShadow (or shavings of a lavender powder shadow) blended with a few drops of any moisturizer such as the *Adrien Arpel Skin Correction Creme with Alpha Hydroxy.* Apply the lavender camouflager over your entire face *before* you apply your Foundation. Let it settle a moment or two before continuing.

Tip: The lavender camouflager is also good for masking broken blood vessels or dilated capillaries. This also works on brownish hyper-pigmentation patches resulting from pregnancy, the Pill, the sun, and/or the aging process.

COLD & FLU COVER UPS

If you can't stay in bed to take care of your cold or flu and must venture forth for work or social obligations, you'll appreciate these suggestions. Put on your Foundation as usual. *Then* pat concealer onto the reddened areas, sealing everything in place by patting on pressed or loose powder. Brush off any excess. If that doesn't quite do it, try this: use a pale greenish-blue or lavender color-correcting concealer to counteract the red. Stroke it on the affected area and then blot off any excess. Apply your Foundation and fix everything with your powder. Has your *code in the node* really attacked and left you with chapping? Just before you go to bed, open up a Vitamin E capsule and spread its oil all over your nose.

COVERUPS TO USE
AFTER YOU APPLY YOUR FOUNDATION

Many of the flaws in this area are those that can be corrected by contouring techniques. As you'll see, contouring can correct an almost limitless number of imperfections. Contouring, however, is a more advanced procedure than cover-up camouflage and it will take practice to master its subtleties. Even though the paraphrased childhood ropejumping ditty below implies its easy, it does take a bit of effort to become Contour Competent.

> "A bit of color, a dab of paint,
> "Make imperfections what they ain't!"

Contouring products to minimize flaws should be a matte taupe (brownish) shade without a trace of orange or pink. Contouring to highlight or maximize good features should be beige, pale pink or white. And, remember the words used in the ditty, above—"bit" and "dab"—not globs and blobs.

Tip: Brush on powders or use large, soft pencils if you have normal or oily skin; cremes and liquids applied with the fingertips, for skin on the dry side. Feel free to experiment, to see what looks and works best for you.

BROAD JAWLINE/WIDE FACIAL STRUCTURE OR NARROW JAW

To correct broad or wide facial structure, use a large, fat brush to sweep a dark powder shadow from just below the ear, down and across the jaw line, under the chin and back up and across the other side of the face, to the bottom of the other ear. To offset a narrow facial structure, follow the same procedure using a highlighter. If you're using creme or powdery creme products, use a dry sponge to apply, following the procedures described above.

Tip: After dipping your brush into your camouflaging powder shadow, tap the brush to shake off loose powder. It's easier to put on more color than it is to remove it if you've been heavy-handed.

SLACK JAWLINE

To offset a slack or somewhat puffed jawline, raise your chin and, with a fat brush, smooth a taupe colored powder right on the jaw line, at and slightly under the jaw and chin, from the ear to the point of the chin. Repeat on the other side. Blend with the brush or your fingertips. If you're using creme or powdery creme products, use a dry sponge to apply, following the procedures described above.

BROAD FOREHEAD

Apply a dark shader about one inch wide from the temple to the brow on each side of your face. Don't forget to blend the edges.

LONG FACE

To shorten a long face, dab some blush on your temples. Use lots of lash thickener and Mascara on your lashes as well as shadowing your lids properly so that other people's eyes will be drawn to your eyes.

Tip: Wear earrings made of metals or stones for the illusion of width.

ROUND FACE

To elongate a round face, apply a two inch vertical stripe on each side of your face, from just below your cheekbone, down to your jawbone. Remember to blend well with your finger tips.

Tip: To make your face look even narrower, wear earrings with a dull surface such as wood, matte-finished plastic, shells.

DOUBLE CHIN

With taupe contouring powder and a fat brush, with contouring creme, or with contouring powdery creme and a dry sponge, make a triangular shape, starting at the center of the chin, with one side of the triangle on each side of the chin and the base of the triangle running along the imaginary line where your neck starts (parallel to the tip of the chin).

BROAD, CROOKED OR LONG NOSE

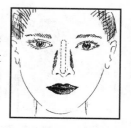

* To slim down a broad nose, run your taupe shader down each side of the nose. Run a light shader along the center of the nose, from the space between the eyes, to the tip of the nose. Blend well.

* To shorten a nose that's a bit too long, apply the taupe powder or creme underneath the tip of the nose, between the nostrils. Also, place a dab of highlighting creme or powder on the top of the nose, below the level of the EyeBrows. Be sure to blend each area well.

* To straighten a crooked nose, pinpoint the "fault line" and smooth a lighter powder or a creme concealer along the side of the nose, opposite the fault. Apply the taupe concealer onto the fault area. Remember: dark to minimize; light to highlight.

- To create a perky, tilted-up nose, put a little dot of light shader or concealer on the center of the tip of the nose, right above the nostrils.

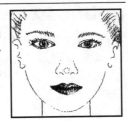

RECEDING CHIN

To bring a receding chin to the fore, dab a small circle of pale pink or white highlighting creme or a Foundation lighter than your basic Foundation on the center of the chin. Smooth a darker shade under the chin, just below the lightened area.

HEAVY-SET EYES

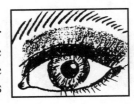

To offset eyes with a heavy eyebone, apply a darker shade to the lower lid; a lighter shade across the top of the lid, to a depth of about 1/8" below the brow. Blend well, especially where the two shades overlap.

CLOSE-SET EYES

To give the illusion of width to closely set eyes, a lighter contouring shade is placed on the lids above the half of the eye closest to the nose. A taupe shader is applied on the lids above the outside corners of the eye.

WIDE APART EYES

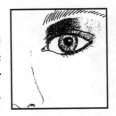

To give a narrower look to eyes that are set too wide apart, place the taupe shader on the lids above the area of the eyes closest to the nose. Apply the lighter shade to the lids above the outer corners of the eyes.

SHAPELESS OR UNEVEN LIPS

This requires experimenting and practice. Examine your lips so that you know exactly what correction is needed. Look at lip shapes in all kinds of beauty magazines and books. Once you've selected the shape you like and think will look well on your face, powder the lip area well with the shade closest to your Foundation. Pencil in the outline of your dream lips with a sharp lip pencil. Start at the center of the top lip, outline to the outer corner in one smooth motion. Repeat on the other side. On the bottom lip, start at one corner and in one smooth sweep, outline all the way to the other corner. Fill in with your favorite Lipstick shade.

 To correct thin lips, take your pencilled outline outside your own lipline. Filling in the upper lip with a frosted Lipstick will give the illusion of fuller lips.

 To correct lips that are too full, draw your pencilled outline inside your natural lip line. Don't use extremely dark or light colors and stay away from frosted lip colors.

Tip: Use more intense colors on smaller lips.

CROW'S FEET

One way to keep your crow's feet in check is to make sure the under-eye area is kept moisturized. You might consider using my very popular *Line Softening Stick* with slow- and fast-absorbing oils to use over or under your Foundation. In addition to keeping the crow's feet area soft and dewy-looking, you'll slow down the appearance of even more of these dreaded lines.

Tip: To keep your CoverUp from exaggerating the crinkles around your eyes, use a line-softener made for the eyes before you apply your concealer. If you still feel the whole world knows that you are wearing concealer, try this. Take out an eyeliner brush and a foundation two shades lighter than your regular foundation. Paint a convering line of the lighter foundation over the lines on your face. Blend very well. This will not work on under-eye circles.

FOUNDATIONS—
THE CANVAS FOR YOUR MAKEUP ART

The purpose of Foundation is to give your skin a flawless finish, smooth and ready for the application of the cosmetic colors onto the features that define your face and distinguish it from all others. Foundation also completes the process started with your base: evening out your skin tones. And, if your Foundation contains a sun screen, its also a protective covering for your skin. The better your skin, the lighter the Foundation you can wear.

SKIN TYPES

The toughest part of getting your Foundation right is determining what type of skin you really have and what shade it is. When it comes to skin types, there are three broad categories: normal; oily or combination; dry or wrinkled; problem (blemished or broken out). If you have normal skin, you have your choice of Foundations and can use whatever formulation is easiest for you to use. Change your Foundation with the change in seasons or keep the same type year in, year out.

OILY SKIN: Use a water-based liquid, applied with the fingertips.

DRY SKIN: Use an oil-based formula, applied with the fingertips. Because the oil in liquids tends to separate, I suggest you use a creme. You'll get easy coverage, as well as softness.

PROBLEM SKIN

> **DRY BLEMISHED:** Use a compact creme applied with a sponge

> **OILY BROKEN OUT:** Use a liquid glycerine powder, applied with the fingertips.

COMBINATION SKIN: Use two types of Foundation: water-based for the oily "T" zone and oil-based for the rest of your face. Or use oil-free Foundation all over; once it's set, dab a moist sponge onto the dry areas of your face.

Tip: Wear less foundation as you get older—foundation is wrinkle-seeking, crease-seeking and line-seeking. You may not see those "fault lines," but believe me, you foundation will. If you want a natural-looking, flawless finish and prefer creme, try the *Adrien Arpel Underglow—No MakeUp, MakeUp*. Or if you prefer powder, try *Kaleidoscope*—a real silk brightening, finishing powder that can be worn alone as a skin finisher or over MakeUp to replace old-fashioned powder.

You can ascertain what kind of Foundation you have purchased by a simple test. Put some of your Foundation on a small plate. Mix with one or two drops of water. It's water-based if it mixes easily. If it doesn't mix well, it's oil-based. Still not sure? Repeat the process using a vegetable oil instead of the water. If the oil mixes easily with your Foundation, you have an oil-based or oleophilic Foundation. If it doesn't mix well, your Foundation is hydrophilic or water-based.

SKIN COLOR

Once you've determined which formulation is right for your skin type, you'll want to address the issue of color. It may be necessary to mix two or even three shades of Foundation to get the best color for your skin. And, you may have to do it more than once a year. Even though you wrap yourself up like a mummy when you go outdoors in the warmer weather, some of the sun's light will reach your skin and *voila*, your skin tones will deepen somewhat. Besides, after six months, if you haven't used up your Foundation, you'll want to use a fresh, contamination-free product anyway.

Tip: Color-test the Foundation on your face, *not on your hands*. Make sure your skin is super clean. Apply the Foundation color at your jawline and let it dry. If you can see a patch of color easily, the shade you selected is not close enough to your own skin color. As the Little Kite was told: "Try, Try again!" The skin under your jaw may be somewhat lighter than your cheeks and you'll want to select a product that works with both areas. Do not, I repeat, *do not* let the cosmetics sales person convince you that the skin on your wrist is the same as that on your face. Insist on trying new shades on your face.

FOUNDATION COLOR

If you are 100% satisfied with the skin tones nature gave you, you can just choose a Foundation shade that matches your own natural shade. But, most of us aren't that lucky or even if we are, we're rarely satisfied with what we were dealt. Fortunately, with the magic of

MakeUp, we can pretty much offset real or imagined color imperfections. But please, if you're a Latin American beauty don't try to achieve a pale, wan Ophelia face, and if your heritage includes tones of delicate English porcelain, stick to the lighter end of the Foundation color spectrum.

- To brighten sallow/yellow skin — use warm, rosy shades
- To tone down ruddiness — use beige or peach shades
- To liven up dark olive skin — use bronze-toned shades
- To warm up pale, delicate skin — use ivories or very pale peach.

Women of color should avoid pink-tone Foundations because they will turn muddy-looking; and, too much yellow in the Foundation will give your skin a drab, ashy look. In general, it's best to select a shade as close to your own natural skin tones as possible, with only a small amount of rose, beige or bronze to warm up or cool down the color Nature selected for you.

APPLYING YOUR FOUNDATION

Use a headband or a towel to get your hair away from your face. Dab little dots of Foundation on your face at the nose, cheeks, chin, temple, eyelids, lips and between your brows. Blend with long, sweeping strokes. Different beauty professionals have different application techniques—some say work up and outward from the center of the face. I believe it's best to smooth Foundation downward for the most even look. That way, the downy facial hairs lie flat. Another benefit of stroking downward is that your Foundation will not disappear into your pores. All in all, top to bottom application gives a more polished finish to the face.

There's no disagreement when it comes to blending though. We all say "Blend blend, blend". Reach behind your ears, over your eyelids and curving slightly up into your nostrils. Unless you don't mind makeup all over the necklines of your dresses and blouses, do not apply Foundation to your throat. End at the natural separation line under the chin, where the chin meets your neck. Blot the area ever so slightly with a tissue.

Tip: When applying Foundation to the super delicate area under your eyes, you should use your pinky. Place one dot of Foundation under each eye and use light, feathery strokes to smooth. Be sure to avoid pulling or dragging the Foundation across this very delicate area.

Quick-Change Foundation Problems

Even if you've done everything right to this point, a moment will probably come when the Foundation in the jar or bottle is no longer what it was. It gets thicker or thinner or off color. Short of chucking the container into the trashcan, is there anything you can do to save the product you spent your hard-earned dollars on? Of course. Just because my name is on the Adrien Arpel products doesn't mean I dump my cosmetics because they've developed a slight deficiency. (Usually I don't have the time to round up replacements while I'm traveling or otherwise involved. Besides, I have a thrifty nature!) So, here a few tricks I've learned or heard about over the years.

- ◆ **Quick-Change — Foundation Not Sheer Enough:** You're already using a lightweight Foundation and it gives you more color/coverage than you want. In the palm of your hand, mix equal parts of your Foundation and de-fizzed seltzer water or mineral water *sans* salt. Apply as usual.

- ◆ **Quick-Change — Foundation Too Watery:** You're out of luck. There really is no way to thicken it. The only thing to do is get a new Foundation. But, don't throw away the runny product. You can use it to get a bit of color on the skin when you're wearing a low-cut dress. If it's the right shade, you can also use it to hide strap marks from your bathing suit. Don't try it on your face, though. You'll just get streaking and, because it doesn't spread evenly, you'll get poor coverage.

- ◆ **Quick-Change — Mixing Foundations:** Basically, you should only mix up enough product to use in one application. It's better not to add different ingredients right into your bottle or jar of Foundation. Three weeks from now, you may not want to use what you mixed today. Nature gave you the perfect palette for mixing a small amount—the palm of your hand.

- ◆ **Quick-Change — Foundation Too Thick:** If you discover that the Foundation you just purchased is too thick, you don't have to trek back to the store to exchange it. Just put one application's worth in the palm of your hand and blend in a little glycerine. If the Foundation remaining in your jar has thickened with time, stir a bit of glycerine into the jar with a coffee stirrer. Or, if it's New Year's Day and there's a bit of champagne left over, add a few drops to any too-thick Foundation lying around. It's a great diluter because it contains carbonic acid, which is good for your skin.

- **QUICK-CHANGE – FOUNDATION TOO GREASY:** Foundation that is too greasy can be salvaged. For very greasy formulations, added a drop or two of witch hazel to a few drops of Foundation in the palm of your hand. For Foundation that's only a wee bit greasy, use a few drops of toner mixed into the Foundation.

- **QUICK-CHANGE – DISAPPEARING FOUNDATION:** If your Foundation gets a shiny look before the end of the day, your UnderBase is probably too moist. That, or you didn't give it time to set properly before applying your Foundation. If you're using a creme UnderBase, first try lengthening the setting time. If that doesn't work, apply less UnderBase. Still suffering from see-through MakeUp before the end of the day—switch to a liquid UnderBase. If your Foundation does the disappearing trick and you're already wearing a liquid UnderBase, try a long-lasting oil-free Glycerine Liquid Powder Foundation. That should eliminate the need for frequent Foundation touch-ups during the day. By the way, your Foundation, properly applied, should provide all-day coverage without the need for reapplication.

- **QUICK-CHANGE –**
FOUNDATION WITH WRINKLE-AFFINITY: When your Foundation seeks out your wrinkles like a heat-seeking missile, you probably went to your high school prom longer ago than you want to share with anyone. The best thing to do is invest in more treatment products to soften your skin. I would suggest you consider adding two light-weight under-eye gels—one for day, one for night, and the *Adrien Arpel Skin Correction Complex: 4 Cremes in One with Alpha Hydroxy*—Day Creme, Night Creme, Moisturizer, Wrinkle Creme. Make sure that you let each product set before you continue. And, as I mentioned at the beginning of this category, use less Foundation. Personally, I prefer a very sheer Foundation.

Incidentally, if you can't find precisely the color you're looking for, be a MakeUp Magician yourself. Don't be afraid to try things, play around with textures and colors until you get what you want. In general you'll want to mix cremes with cremes, oils with oils, liquids with liquids and so on. The exception to the rule is powder. Powders can be mixed and blended with almost any product. For example, most liquid MakeUps contain powdery compounds. Watch for the *Adrien Arpel Powdery Creme Custom Mix Compacts* being demonstrated on television. They contain four colors and a lavender UnderBase so you can blend to perfection.

- ◆ **QUICK-CHANGE — FOUNDATIONS TOO DRAB:** If your Foundation leaves your skin looking dull, you may want to add something to brighten it up. For a rosy color, shave some pink powder blush or EyeShadow into your Foundation. Want to look like a ripe Georgia peach? Add some grains of apricot EyeShadow.

- ◆ **QUICK-CHANGE — FOUNDATION TOO BROWN:** Some pink blusher scrapings will lighten your liquid or creme Foundation. Make sure you blend well before you apply the concoction to your face.

- ◆ **QUICK-CHANGE — PARTY FOUNDATION NEEDED:** If you want some sparkle and shine for an evening event, try blending a drop or two or shavings of frosted or pearlized white or an extremely pale lavender EyeShadow into your Foundation. Want more drama? Use a very small amount of gold, bronze or silver shadow. Caution! If you suffer from pimple pop-cuts, or have oily skin, skip the luminescence and stick to a matte finish. Shiny formulations just highlight pimples and oily patches.

- ◆ **QUICK-CHANGE — FOUNDATION FOR JOGGING, ETC.:** For a bit of coverage while you're engaged in active sports, use this trick. In the palm of your hand, mix equal parts of my *Skin Correction Complex : 4 In One Creme* or some other Moisturizer if you don't already have mine, with Foundation. Alternate: mix a few shavings of a bronze EyeShadow into a small amount of moisturizer in the palm of your hand. Either mixture will give you just enough coverage to feel "dressed" should you encounter neighbors or that jogger with the sexy you-know-whats.

- ◆ **QUICK-CHANGE — SUMMERIZING/WINTERIZING:** If your winter foundation is too light for your summer skin coloring, you could buy a new bottle of Foundation. But, you could also become an instant Alchemist. To a liquid Foundation, add a few drops of a liquid bronzer. Use a brown contouring creme to summerize your Foundation if it's is a creme. If you've disregarded all of the warnings about what the sun can do to your skin and you have acquired a dark tan check out the Foundations made especially for Women of Color. Get a small size of one of these, which are available in many shades made specifically to enhance the depth and lushness of black skin. Add a few drops at a time to your Foundation until you reach the shade that matches your tan. Conversely, if you purchased your Foundation in the Summer and the first snowfall has been predicted for tonight, don't panic. Just mix a little bit of talcum powder in your palm with Foundation each time you apply it, to lighten and brighten your Summer Foundation.

- **QUICK-CHANGE — STREAKY FOUNDATION, ETCETERA:** If your eyes were *not* fully open when you applied your Foundation, you don't have to wash your face and start the whole process again. Just dampen a clean cosmetic sponge with a small amount of water and stroke it over your entire face, with downward strokes. In fact if, when you check the mirror, you discover any of the "goofs" listed below, you can correct them by blending and smoothing with that same damp cosmetic sponge.

  - too much Foundation in your crow's feet, along side your nose, between your lips and your chin
  - demarcation line at the jawline or near your hairline
  - the area above the lip not blended properly
  - no Foundation on the lips
  - no Foundation on tip of the nose, eyelids or earlobes

You should check your Foundation as soon as you've finished applying it—while it's still damp. It's much easier to touch up mistakes when it's moist than it is if you wait until it's completely dry. Even a moist applicator sponge can't help even things out once the Foundation is totally dry. Naturally, there's an exception to this rule, too. Re-blend the area around your nostrils, where liquids have a tendency to puddle. Use your fingertips for the best results. By the way, if you forgot to put Foundation on your eyelids, you'll probably be complaining that your EyeShadow doesn't stay on. Same with the lips. Eye and lip color, as well as blush, clings better to Foundation than it does to your skin and will look much more even. Don't believe it? Try doing one eyelid, one cheek and one side of your mouth with Foundation underneath the rest of your MakeUp and one lid, the opposite cheek and the other side of the mouth without. You'll see the difference very quickly.

Tip: To wake up a worn-out sponge MakeUp applicator, soak it overnight in a solution of 1 cup warm water to which 1 teaspoon of baking soda has been added. In the morning, rinse the applicator in cool, clear water and you're all set with a fresh sponge.

Once you've completed the application of your Foundation and made all the corrections, give your face a few minutes to "set". Get into the habit of doing a two or three minute task so you don't rush the setting process, i.e., put on your stockings, run an emery board over your nails, put on your earrings, read your Horoscope or check the 5-Day Weather Forecast. Okay, now spritz your face with cold mineral water, sprayed from a plant atomizer or the kind of spray bottle your hairstylist uses to keep your hair wet while he or she is cutting it. This simple step will keep your makeup looking fresh hours longer. It will also help your Powder Blushers and Shadows cling to your face better.

BLUSHERS—THE BIG "D"

The Big "D" stands for the Big "Difference". Without Blushers, the effectiveness of your total look would be diminished greatly. Besides giving you the glow of health, instantly, Blushers give shape to your face, make you look alive and three-dimensional. And Powders, which we'll discuss at the end of this chapter, are used to "set" everything that was put on your face before this "finishing" product. Before we get into which Blushers and Powders to use and exactly where to apply what, you must invest in a thick, fluffy Blush brush, as well as a translucent Powder brush. The results you'll get will be worth every penny you spend on it. "Can't I use the same brush for both?" you ask. "No!" say I. First of all, you'd be transferring color from one to the other and end up with gobs of Blusher on your nose and a flattened out look on your cheeks. Besides, a Blush brush needs a curved top, while the Powder brush needs a flat top.

WHICH BLUSHER IS FOR ME?

You have to consider your skills in blending cosmetics on your face. If you think you're an utter klutz when it comes to achieving a smooth look with powders, do try the *Adrien Arpel True Blush*. Regular Powder Blushers are the most difficult to blend because once they're on your face, it's very hard to push those little granules around. Of course, with the cremes and liquids, you won't be able to get a true matte look. If you own a Powder Blush, be sure to moisturize your skin very well in the cheek area underneath the Blusher, making every effort to blend properly. I think it's worth making the effort to learn how to use Powder Blushers because they last longer. Believe me, with some practice, you can learn. Just start with a small amount of Blusher in the beginning. It's easier to add more; difficult to remove without going back to square one.

Tip: Blushers in powder form are applied after you've applied your face powder. Liquid, creme or gel Blushers are applied over the Foundation but under the face powder.

WHAT COLOR BLUSHER?

As with all color products, you'll need to remember the rule when you're making your Blusher color selection: Highlight or maximize good features; darken to minimize negative features. In general, Women of Color should steer clear of pale pinks, pale peach and white-based mauve blushes. The most flattering shades for women of color with skin in the middle range, are coppers, rusts, deep orange, brown mauve, deep burgundy or clear red. For women of any skin color—the lighter your complexion is, the lighter your Blusher should be. Pink and peach work well with complexions in the fair range. Clear reds work for virtually anyone. Bronzes and earth tones are suitable for all but the palest beauty. Darker complexions are flattered by mauve Blushers. Blushers that are very frosty or heavily pearlized should be saved for evening events when subtle lighting calls for a bit of shine and sparkle. One product I recommend you try is the *True Blush* which I've recently created to help women deal with the "What color should my Blusher be" question. The *Adrien Arpel True Blush* is a combination of tiny pastel-colored spheres that work in synergy. When they're applied, the create a truly natural, soft-looking cheek color. *True Blush* is "mistake-proof", extremely easy to apply and is the one Blusher that will go with any color you wear.

Tip: By the way, Blusher colors with lots of yellow in them are not flattering to any skin tones.

Exactly Where Do I Put The Blusher?

"Where, oh where do I put the blusher" is probably the most frequently asked question when it comes to make-up how-to instructions. If it's too high on the cheeks you'll end up with an unattractive flat look. In addition, you'll be drawing attention to under-eye bags, dark shadows and crow's feet. If it's too low, it will "pull your face down", making you look older. And lastly, don't put your Blusher too close to your nose or everyone will focus on your nose rather than on your face's more attractive features.

You may have heard the expression "the apple of your cheek". That's the spot you want to locate. "Easier said than done" you say.

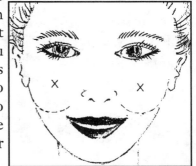

If you're a Grandma, do you pinch the cheeks of your grandchildren with much affection. That's the spot. If you're not in the Grandmother category yet, you probably still remember where your's pinched you. In case there are no Grandmas around, here's an easy way to find the "apple". Smile the biggest smile you can smile. Locate the very center or highest point of your cheeks. That's it!

For Powder Blusher: Apply cheek color to the "apple" and sweep the Blush brush diagonally up and out from the center of your cheek towards your ear. Blend so the amount of color diminishes as you get closer to the hairline near the ear.

For Creme, Gel or Liquid Blushers: Dab a dot of color on the "apple" of your cheek. Place another dot along an imaginary

diagonal line one inch below the first dot. Place a third dot one inch above the first dot, along that same imaginary line. Blend outwards, towards the hairline.

Tip: To give yourself a "visual face lift", align a fourth dot of Blusher with the outer edge of your EyeBrow and blend it towards the top of your ear.

- **QUICK-CHANGE — TOO-DARK BLUSHER:** Dip your Blush brush into translucent powder (pressed or loose). Next, dip your brush into (or across) your Blusher and apply it to your face as described previously. This will also work if you have problems creating natural-looking cheeks.

- **QUICK-CHANGE — LINE OF DEMARCATION:** To eliminate any lines where your powder Blusher ends and your skin tones begin, run a barely damp cosmetic sponge across the demarcation. Or, apply the *Adrien Arpel Kaleidoscope* all over your face, right over the Blush. It will blend it all together.

- **QUICK-CHANGE — LIGHT & DARK:** Need a Powder Blusher slightly lighter than the one you generally use? Mix some cornstarch or talcum powder with the Blusher. Want a deeper shade for a more dramatic look? Mix your Blusher with some dark mauve or bronze EyeShadow.

- **QUICK-CHANGE — MODEL'S CHEEKBONES:** If you've always felt Mother Nature deprived you of haughty high cheek bones, now's your chance to have them, or the illusion thereof. (You may decide that Ma Nature knew what she was doing after all; but, it doesn't hurt to try.) Make a "fish face" by sucking in your cheeks. Find the hollow under the cheek bones. Apply a dab of darker Blusher right there. Stroking outwards, away from the center of your face along the under side of your cheekbones, blend well. Now, following the "apple method" described earlier, apply your regular color Blusher. Blend with the darker under-cheek color. No line of demarcation should be visible.

- **QUICK-CHANGE — A BRIGHTER OUTLOOK:** Want to brighten your overall look? Dab your Blush brush lightly on the tip of your nose, your chin and across your forehead.

- **QUICK-CHANGE — NO STAYING POWER:** If your Blush seems to disappear or if it doesn't last the day, smooth a very thin coating of petroleum jelly under the Blush. You'll eliminate the problem immediately. An alternate method is to use both a creme and a powder formulation. First apply a creme (or liquid) Blush in the approved manner. Let it dry completely. Then, using the same (or similar) color powder Blusher, stroke it across the first layer of color. It's guaranteed to last 'til you remove it.

◆ **Quick-Change—For a MakeUp Refresher:** A few hours after you've applied your MakeUp, your face begins to look dry. Do you have to re-do your entire face? Not at all. Just dab of the *Adrien Arpel Skin Correction Complex 4-In-One Creme* or a little moisturizer over your cheek bones. Your makeup will look fresh again.

EyeBrows—
High Brow, Low Brow, Best Brow

More than anything, EyeBrows are the frame not only of your eyes, but also for the painting that is your face. Through the ages, from apewoman to today's fashion magazine covergirl, EyeBrows have played an important role. At first, when they were low down on the face, EyeBrows were a hairy, protective shield meant to keep irritants such as pollen and dust particles away from the eyes. As we evolved, our brains grew in size, in effect placing the brows higher up on the forehead. Before long, our brows had no shielding purpose because they were truly "high brows", a result of our greater intelligence.

Soon, fashion pace-setters latched onto the EyeBrows to use in making fashion statements. And of course, as with all fashion, change has become an integral part of presenting EyeBrows to the world. Over the years, Fashion dictated: thick brows; straight brows; skinny, highly plucked brows; shaved brows (not a recent invention, as you can see in paintings in both the Middle Ages and again in the 18th Century); high-arched brows with a perpetual expression of surprise built right into the brows; even tattooed EyeBrows. Incidentally, Charles Darwin points out that the EyeBrows are actually not raised to express surprise. We're just opening our eyes wider, causing the muscle above the eye to go upwards, in turn making the brows go up. By the year 3100 A.D., if some of the science fiction shows have any basis in fact, we may well be altogether browless. In the meantime, the question is: "How do I wear my brows."

In my opinion, the current trend of looking natural, a look which is never totally out of style, is the best brow look. With a natural brow as a basis, minor changes can keep you looking fashionable. An ancient American Indian greeting is "Walk in Balance". And, as far as EyeBrows are concerned, that's what you should be looking for in a brow. Brows should be in balance with the rest of your facial features and the shape of your face. Not wild and bushy and not thin as a single pencil line. If you're seriously considering an extreme brow, let me share one fact which may keep you natural-looking. There's nothing that dates a woman faster than the shape of her brows or the color of her EyeShadow. You can be sure that the woman with the skinny, skinny old movie star brows, learned how to apply makeup when Gloria Swanson and Jean Harlowe were at the peak of their perfection. And the lady with the bright, bright blue EyeShadow all over her lids, went to her high school prom in the early 50s. If that's what you see when you take a long, hard look at yourself in the mirror, consider a change. Unless of course, you don't care who knows exactly when you were born. (As you probably know, I don't mind telling my age because I know I don't look as old as I am. But I wouldn't want someone who doesn't know me to look at me and guess the exact day I was born just by looking at my brows or EyeShadow!)

Of course, some people came into the world with brows that are near perfect—the right color, the right number of hairs per inch of brow and the right placement. If you're one of those lucky ones, all you'll have to do is pluck a straggler here and there, once in a while, and occasionally brush the hairs above the inner corner of your eyes upwards, on a daily basis. But for those of us upon whom Mom Nature did not smile when she was handing out EyeBrows, you'll have to pinch hit for her. Incidentally, as we age, our brows lose hair and shape.

To Pluck Or Not To Pluck

If your eyes are too bushy or there are more brow hairs then you want, you'll have to decide whether to have your brows waxed or whether to have them tweezed (or tweeze them yourself). By the way, do not shave your EyeBrows; do not use chemical depilatories near your eyes; and, while electrolysis works—like a diamond, it's forever.

Of the two acceptable methods of removing EyeBrows, waxing is much faster; but, with tweezing you have much more control. You make the decision as to exactly which hairs come out and which stay in. If you are very fussy, control counts for a lot. Some other factors you might want to consider in your decision-making process: waxing gives a much cleaner, very "perfect" look. It takes about 10 minutes and needs to be done every three to six weeks. I don't recommend doing this at home.

1. Wax that's too hot can burn you.
2. You can easily remove more hair than you want to.
3. If you're using Retin-A or a similar product, there can be an adverse reaction.

Tweezing will take 20 to 30 minutes. The first time, you should have it done professionally to get it exactly right. After all, you don't want to end up with one short, fat brow and another one that's long and skinny. Or no brows at all. It takes three months for a full set of brows to grow in. The hair on your brows grows about ten times more slowly than the hair on your head. After the first tweezing session, you can keep your brows looking very natural by checking for re-growth once or twice a week and removing the hairs as they re-appear. Or, you can let them go and return for a professional EyeBrow arch every 6 to 8 weeks. Continuous tweezing may ultimately cause the hairs to grow more slowly. This results from the damage that tweezing may cause in the follicle, where the hair root resides.

If you absolutely have to do your first brow tweezing yourself, invest in a good pair of tweezers. Then, using pencils, place one so it runs alongside your nose and the inner corner of your eye. Where the pencil crosses your brow, is where your EyeBrow should start. To find the spot where your brow should end line up another pencil from the bottom side of the nostril to the outer corner of the eye. Anything beyond that point should be tweezed away. If your eyes are very small and close set, you can make them appear to be wider apart by starting 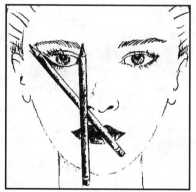 your brow at the point halfway between the inner corner of your eye and your eyeball (when you're looking straight ahead). How do you know if your eyes are too close together? It's easy. Measure your eye, from the inner corner to the outer corner. Then, measure the space between your eyes (over your nose). If the length between your eyes is less than the length of one eye, your eyes are closer together than the "norm". Eyes that are set wider apart than the "norm" are usually considered to be exotic. So, Ms. Wide Eyes, unless you have a burning desire to be normal, enjoy Nature's gift to you.

TOOLS FOR "THE BROW-MEISTER"

As with virtually everything one does, the proper tools make the difference between professional-looking results and a so-so finish. Yes, you can do without some of these tools. But, if you're serious about wanting to look better, younger and more attractive, don't be chintzy when it comes to the equipment you use.

1. Stiff EyeBrow Brush (or a Child's Toothbrush—Hard)
2. EyeBrow Comb for defining (Optional, except for women with very ample EyeBrows)
3. Precision Eyebrow Tweezers
4. EyeBrow Pencil and/or EyeBrow Powder with an angled Brow Applicator Brush

THE WHEN, WHERE AND WHAT

Since there's always some reddening and irritation when you tweeze, the best time to tackle this job is right after you've taken your evening shower—when the pores are open from the hot water. It's also a good idea to tweeze just before you go to bed or when you know you won't be going anywhere for a few hours. Why? It's better *not* to apply MakeUp for several hours after tweezing your brows. Before you begin, brush your brows upwards, all the way across; then, brush them back the other way. Use an EyeBrow brush or an old toothbrush. Next, dip your tweezers in alcohol and run an alcohol-moistened cotton ball over your brows. By the way, you can sharpen your tweezers by running them across some sandpaper several times. Now you're ready to start.

Pluck the straggly hairs from between your brows and those beyond the ending point first. Once you've eliminated the hairs between both eyes and at the outer edges, you'll need to approach the hairs on the lower side of your brows. Where do you start? Don't panic. Close your eyes and run your fingers across your EyeBrow to locate the bony structure right beneath the hair line. All the hairs that lie below that should be removed. Tweeze from the center, outwards, grasping each hair at the root and plucking in the direction in which the hair grows. Stretch the skin taut, between the thumb and index finger from beneath the brow, plucking one hair at a time.

You could use a concealer stick to draw in a shape, just to get an idea of how thick your brows should be and how much of an arch you want *before* you actually pluck. Incidentally, the high point of the arch should be above the center of your pupil or slightly towards its outer edge. Make sure you have good lighting, otherwise you'll end up pinching your skin or gouging yourself. Go easy. You can always pluck more hairs. But, they won't grow back quickly if you tweeze too many on the first go-around. When you're finished, brush your brows— upwards over the inner corner of the eye; as the hairs grown along the rest of the brow. Check the mirror and tweeze away any leftovers so you obtain a clean, natural looking, well-shaped brow.

IN GENERAL, DO NOT TWEEZE THE HAIRS ABOVE YOUR BROW LINE.

You can also use EyeBrow re-shaping to give the illusion that a round face is more oval, a long face is shorter or make your eyes appear larger. To achieve a more oval look, if your face is too round, make the arch more pronounced. That means making the arc of the curve a bit higher and starting it just before you get to the spot in line with the center of your pupil. To "shorten" a face that's too long, do not arch your brows at all; "run them" straight across the top of your eyes, from corner to corner. And, if your upper eyelid is on the small side, pluck out an additional row of hairs along the bottom brow line to give the appearance of more open space.

Tip: If your pain threshold is lower than sea level, there are a few things you can do to ease the ouch. You can:

- ◆ use a baby's teething preparation to numb the brow area
- ◆ soften the brow hairs with shaving creme so they'll come out more easily
- ◆ run an ice cube covered with a paper towel, along the brow— you may have to repeat a few times if you don't really have the art of tweezing in hand

Before I teach you how to use brow products, I'd like you to review the appearance of your newly tweezed EyeBrows. If you've done the job right, your brows will be like a picture frame—it's there; but you barely are aware of it. But, like a picture frame if it's crooked or the wrong size, EyeBrows that are not right, throw everything else out of kilter.

- • Your brows should have only minor variations in thickness along their entire length. They can be ever-so-slightly tapered from the highest point of the brow to the end—but only slightly.

* The highest point or arch of the brow should be above the area between the center of your pupil and its outer edge. Experiment until you find the exact spot that's most flattering to you.

Daily EyeBrow Regimen

Every day, right after you brush your teeth or your hair, brush your EyeBrows to stimulate them and to get rid of any loose hairs. As with the hair on your head, you will loose EyeBrows. Not the 50 to 100 a day that fall from your scalp; but one here and two there, once a day or every third day. It's a normal process; so don't worry. You'll want to brush your brows in three directions.

1. Brush against the grain or from the outer edge towards the bridge of your nose.
2. Brush upwards, towards your forehead.
3. Brush them back into place, in the direction in which they grow.

For a more high fashion look, you can stop after the 2nd step, leaving your EyeBrows standing straight up. This will make your eye appear more wide open. If you like the illusion but don't feel completely comfortable with EyeBrows standing at attention, you can just brush up the hairs in the first inch of your brows on either side of the bridge of your nose. The rest of the brows are brushed back to their natural growth pattern. If the hairs don't stay standing up, get some neutral colored mustache wax, and with the applicator apply the wax to your brushed up brows. You can achieve a similar effect by running a moistened brow brush over some glycerine soap and then brushing your EyeBrows upwards.

To keep your EyeBrows from becoming brittle, every night before you go to bed, coat your EyeBrows with a heavy coat of night creme. Petroleum jelly will also do the trick. If you want to "train" your EyeBrows to grow *a little* differently, while the petroleum jelly is on, brush your EyeBrows in the direction in which you would like them to grow. After a month or so following this regimen, your EyeBrows should be easier to tame during the day. If they're still unruly, you can dab a little hair gel or slicker onto your EyeBrows with your index finger, and comb or brush the hairs until they are lying the way you want them to lie. Another trick—aim some hair spray onto a cotton ball and stroke it over your EyeBrows. *Never, never* spray onto your EyeBrows directly.

Tip: If you're plagued with curly hairs in your EyeBrow, don't despair. Clip them with tiny shears, so the hairs lie against the brow, in the same direction in which they grow.

COLORING YOUR EYEBROWS

You probably always thought that fashionable EyeBrows were made with cosmetics. As you can see from the foregoing, the size and shape of your EyeBrows is determined long before you ever pick up a EyeBrow Pencil or Powder. The next question I'm generally asked is "Shall I use a pencil or a powder to define my EyeBrows?" Actually, you'll probably use both. The Powder to give fullness and enhance your own EyeBrow color; the pencil to make the drawn-in EyeBrow look natural.

Make sure that the EyeBrow pencils and powder you purchase are close to your natural color or the natural-looking hair color only your hairdresser knows about for sure. I'd suggest that you use a shade one degree lighter than your natural/natural-looking hair color. For the most natural-looking EyeBrow color, use two shades of pencil or powder. The second shade would then be the same as your own color. Black should be avoided unless your skin is extremely dark and your haircolor is black or very dark brown. If you're a natural blonde or redhead, your EyeBrows may be extremely light or almost non-existent. In that case, you may have to obtain a super-fine EyeBrow pencil to draw in each hair, one by one. Alternately, seek out an EyeBrow powder formulated for super-thin EyeBrows and apply with tiny, feathery strokes in the direction of the hairs' growth, in essence also drawing in the EyeBrows hair by hair.

To accentuate the shape of your EyeBrows, fill in the sparse areas and the edges with short, diagonal strokes, using a sharp EyeBrow pencil. Follow the growth line. On the first half of the brow—from above the inner corner of the eye—use upward strokes. From the peak of the arch to the end of the EyeBrow (above the outer corner of the eye), use downward strokes. If your EyeBrows do not grow all the way to across your eye, stopping short of the spot above the outer corner of the eye, you can fill in the missing hair with light strokes of a fine EyeBrow pencil. Then, to soften the overall look, brush your Eyebrows lightly.

• EyeBrows that are too thick detract from your eyes.

- EyeBrows which are too thin give the face a flat look and tend to exaggerate any flaws in the area of the eyes—such as puffiness or crow's feet.

- Avoid solid lines, highly arched EyeBrows or too dark Eyebrows— all have a tendency to give you a hard look and to make you look considerably older.

Tip: A fast way to fix EyeBrows that are too dark: rub a dab of foundation on your EyeBrows. A bit of loose face powder, applied sparingly, can also do the job. Then brush them with an old toothbrush.

If you don't want to take the time to practice all of the foregoing, you'll be happy to know that I've developed a new product just for you: *The Brow Maker Kit.* It includes eyebrow stencils that help you shape your brow perfectly. All you have to do is "fill in" your brows with the one or more of the brush-on powders and/or the two EyeBrow pencils which are included in the kit.

EyeLiner—the Trickiest MakeUp Step

Back when I first started wearing MakeUp, somewhere around the age of 14, it took me quite a while until I had the courage to display my work with an EyeLiner to anyone but my sister. The lines I made were too fat, too long, looked like the teeth in *Jaws* mouth, made me look like a raccoon. All of the mistakes I've seen and heard about in my career as the owner of my own cosmetics organization, I made! So, when I tell you, you can learn how to use an EyeLiner effectively, if you're willing to spend a little time practicing, you can believe me. None of us comes to Earth knowing exactly how to apply EyeLiner. If such knowledge were hereditary, I would not have had to watch my daughter, Lauren, struggle the same way I did. And in less than 10 years, I'm sure I'll be watching my granddaughter, who is four years old now, trying to learn the Art of MakeUp. And, she's watched two of the world's most well known experts, Grandma and Mommy putting their faces on for years. It would be nice, wouldn't it, if our kids could learn from our mistakes? Ah well—back to EyeLiners.

To help you develop a good eye lining technique you'll need the proper EyeLiner pencil or liquid EyeLiner brush.

EyeLiner Pencil: The best EyeLiner pencil is one that is firm, yet with lead that's soft enough so it glides across your eyelid without pulling or dragging. You can test the pencil on the pocket of skin between your index finger and your thumb. If it slides easily, without puckering, it should glide along your eyelid.

- **Quick-Change — EyeLiner Lead Not Soft Enough:** You already have some EyeLiner pencils which don't meet the above specifications? Warm them—by holding them near a match or a lighter, or by running hot water over them—to soften them *slightly*. Let them cool for a moment and then draw your lines. Of course, each time you apply MakeUp you'll have to repeat the warming process.

- **Quick-Change — Dull Points:** While EyeLiner pencils must be soft to avoid drag, they must simultaneously be well-sharpened so you can make nice thin lines. *Before you sharpen them*, place them in the freezer for about 15 minutes. That will help to prevent the breakage that frequently occurs while you're getting a fine point.

Liquid EyeLiner Brush: The applicator brush that comes with liquid EyeLiner is usually just right. However, if you find there's a tendency to end up with a thick line above your eyelashes, your applicator may be a little too fat. Using a pair of sharp manicure scissors, trim away a few hairs from the applicator brush. If the line is still too thick, repeat the trimming process until you achieve the thinness you want. You could also visit an art supply store, *with* the offending EyeLiner brush in hand. Find a long-handled artist's brush with bristles that are narrower than those on your applicator brush.

Applying EyeLiner or "Walking" The Straight & Narrow

Whether you decide to apply your EyeLiner with a pencil or a liquid, you'll need a steady hand. It usually takes lots more practice to apply it properly with a liquid liner. But, personally, I think it's worth the effort. If it's your very first time working with a liquid liner, practice controlling the width of the line by drawing lines on the top of your hand. Okay. After you've drawn about 50 short lines on your hand, you'll be ready to try it for real. Prop your elbows on the table to help steady your hand. Later on, when you've achieved a steady, smooth stroke, you'll be able to do it in mid-air. Work outwards from the center of the eye. It is not necessary to run your EyeLiner all the way over to the inner corner of the eye. A spot approximately beneath the center of your pupil should be your starting point. If your eyes are wide apart you can start the line about one-third of the way from the inner corner of the eye. If your eyes are very close together, start at a point just above the outer edge of your eyeball, as you're looking straight ahead. Liner for eyes that measure the same length as the distance from inner eye to inner eye (over the bridge of the nose) should be started at the point slightly to the nose side of the iris. Start with a narrow line, continue the stroke across the lid. To create

the illusion of a slight "lift", get a little wider as you approach the outer corner. Extend the line a fraction beyond the end of the outer corner of the eye, tapering the line away to nothing. There should be no skin showing between the liner and the lashes.

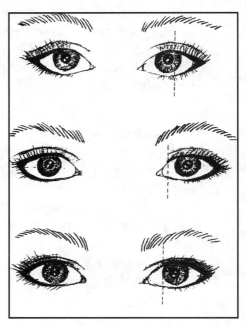

Tip: The older you get, the closer to the outer corner of your eye the EyeLiner should be started. That means if you're 100 years old like my friend Sunny's mother is, you can skip EyeLiner altogether.

If after all of your practice sessions, your EyeLiner brush still walks a crooked line, don't give up. There is a solution. Put away your liquid liner. Put away your fine line pencil. Get a long kohl pencil in black, dark brown or navy blue. Make a row of dots along the lid, right up against the lashes. With a Q-Tip, connect the dots and you'll have a picture of—just kidding—you'll have what appears to be a straight line. Keep the liner on the top of the lid, as close to the lashes as possible.

Special Eyeliner Effects

A trick for giving the illusion that your eyes are larger than they really are—using a red Lip Liner pencil, make a red dot in the very corner of your inner eye lid. One per eye, please.

Don't put a lining ring around your entire eye. It makes your eyes look much smaller than they really are. To add drama *and* to make yourself a wide-eyed look, using a full-sized soft EyeLiner pencil, place a line under the outer one-third of your lower lashes and just outside the outer corner of the eye. Smudge the lines with a Q-Tip for a soft, appealing look.

A remedy for eyes with red, roadmap lines crisscrossing the whites: use a soft, but firm blue pencil to rim the inside of the lower lid, right above and alongside of your lower lashes. The blue color makes white look whiter. (Remember the bluing your Mom used to throw into the final rinse of the wash every Monday? If you don't, I know you're still a Spring Chicken!) Another trick for making small eyes seem to be larger: use an eyes-only white pencil to rim the inside of the lower lid, right next to and inside the lashes.

If your problem is eyes that are too prominent, you can make them seem to be smaller by widening the line you place above your upper eye lashes. The rule: the broader the line, the smaller the eye appears to be.

Who Knows What Product Works on the Eyes of You? *The Shadow Knows*

You've heard me say it before. Nothing gives away age as quickly as your EyeShadow color and style of application. Electric blue Shadow spread all over the eye lids is a sure sign of a gal who hit her teens in the early 1950s. Dark brown or charcoal, with white or pale creme on the lids, tells you she's a '60s Miss. Mauves and pinks all over the entire eye lid mean she started wearing EyeShadow in the late '70s or early '80s. The no-shadow look is evidence that she started using makeup in the '30s or in the mid-to-late 1980s. In this case the number of laugh lines around the eyes will tell you which it is. Nowadays, the neutrals and colors in the brown/beige family are *de riguer*. Bone, creme and eggshell are also in vogue among fashion pace-setters. The nice thing however is that the every-day women need *not* imitate the looks selected by 5'10" size teeny-tiny models to be fashionable.

We can wear updated versions of shadow from our own favorite era or wear modified adaptations of the MakeUp being featured in the fashion publications and wear what looks best on our faces—cosmetic fashions which relate not only to our age and appearance but also to our lifestyles.

On the practical aspects of EyeShadowing, there are a number of problems you could encounter. Not to worry. They're all solved quite easily. The major concerns are: cracking powder shadows; creasing creme shadows; colors that flake off. One of the Adrien Arpel products *Moisturizing Shadow Undercoat*, is a creme base formulated specifically to be worn under your EyeShadow. It's designed to keep your shadows from creasing so quickly, will help your colors stay on longer and also prevent your lids from looking lined and dry.

Like all of Gaul (from your first year high school Latin textbook), your eyelid is divided into three parts when it comes to applying eye MakeUp:

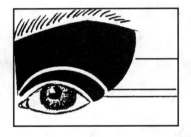

A. The lower lid, which extends from the base of your upper lashes to the imaginary line where the eye socket is indented.

B. The indentation or crease itself—the imaginary line that separates your lower lid from your upper lid.

C. The upper lid, or the skin which covers the bony ridge that lies right above the indentation.

Depending on the configuration of your eyes, different colors will be used on the different parts or on portions of these parts. Before we discuss the "how-to's", let's examine the kinds of EyeShadow products which are available. The different types are:

LOOSE EYESHADOW POWDER: The most difficult to get on your eye lids smoothly.

PRESSED EYESHADOW POWDER: This is easiest to use. It blends well and comes in matte, glossy, frosted or plain. Powder Eye Shadows last on your lids longer than any other kind of Shadow. To increase their staying power even further, Powder EyeShadows can be applied with a moistened applicator brush. This also intensifies the color of the product.

Tube-type Creme EyeShadow: Great colors; but tends to settle into the lines and creases if you aren't wearing an eye UnderBase.

EyeShadow Creme in a Pot: Same problem as the tube-type.

Every EyeShadow will ultimately crease and since we blink our eyes roughly 20 times a minute you can readily understand why. The other enemy of EyeShadow is the natural oils secreted by the skin. They cause the EyeShadow products literally to slide down your lids.

How to Apply EyeShadow – Basic Daytime Look

Creme EyeShadow (Tube or Pot): For a "basic" eye, dab a row of small dots of EyeShadow creme lightly across the lower lid. It's very easy to add more; it's very difficult to remove, without having to go back to the beginning. With a "Q-tip", a sponge applicator or your fingertips, gently blend the dots together, outwards from the inner corner of the eye. Spread the creme from the roots of the upper lashes, upwards and outwards.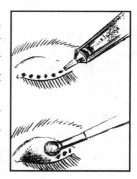

Pressed EyeShadow Powder: Use a blunt, short-handled EyeShadow brush, with bristles slightly less than one inch wide. Stroke your brush along the pressed powder and tap it or blow on the edge, to eliminate the loose powder which will fall onto your cheek bone otherwise. With small, feathery strokes, starting from the inside corner of the eye, brushing upwards and outwards, apply the color over the entire bottom half of the lid, ending on a diagonal line that stretches from 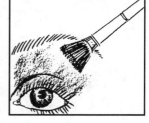 the outer corner of the eye to the spot where your EyeBrow ends.

Loose EyeShadow Powder: Follow the same instructions as for the pressed EyeShadow; but take much smaller quantities. If you don't tap off the excess powder, you'll end up with colored granules all over your face and clothing.

Whichever type of EyeShadow you select, the best thing to do is to experiment to answer the question "Just how much of my lid shall I cover" as well as "What color(s) shall I use". You'll most likely be able to come up with a variety of looks that appeal to you and also maximize your eyes. After all, that's the purpose of wearing EyeShadow to begin with—to make your eyes look their very best.

MAKE THE HAND QUICKER THAN THE EYE

When it comes to applying your EyeShadow, you want your hands to be as deft as those of a magician. And, as it is with the illusions a magician creates, you'll have to practice until you can fool the eyes. Here are some MakeUp tricks you can practice:

* **LARGE EYE TRICKS:** If your eyes are large and wide open, 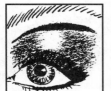 you can try a deep shade on the lower lid with a lighter hue of the same color on the lower two-thirds of the upper lid. Then run a highlighter line from 1/16th to 1/8th inch thick, along the underside of the EyeBrow. For evenings, add a very deep tone from the same family as that on the lower lids, at the very outer corner of the lower lids. Be sure to blend where the colors overlap. It's easier to *do it* than it is to describe it. So, just be patient and practice. To make the eyes look even wider, dab a light colored EyeShadow on the center of your upper lid. Blend—but not too much.

* **SMALL EYE TRICKS:** Use a light shade on the entire lower  lid. Run a deep, smoky color along the indentation line. Stroke a highlighter with a sheen, starting low on the upper lid diagonally outwards, getting broader as you approach the outer edge of the EyeBrow. An EyeLiner in a shade close to the color used on the indentation should be used. Run a narrow line right above the upper lashes, from corner to corner, as well as underneath the outer half of the lower lashes. Use a white eye rimmer inside the lower lashes to enlarge the appearance of the whites of your eyes.

* **DEEP-SET EYES GO FRONT & CENTER:** To give deep-set eyes the illusion of being set more forward than they really

are, you'll have to do the opposite of most EyeShadow application instructions. The light or bright shade is applied on the lower lid. Use a deeper, smokier shade above the indentation, blending upwards and outwards. Apply a blue liner to the inside of your lower lid, to make the whites of your eyes look whiter.

- **TRICKS TO CAMOUFLAGE PROTRUDING EYES:**

To make protruding eyes recede, use colors that give the illusion of receding: dark colors. Start with a dark, but muted color on the lower lid. Use another muted color, a bit darker than the lower lid shade, on the indentation. Don't apply any shadow to your upper lid. Use lots of Mascara—three coats would work well. Apply EyeLiner around the entire eye.

- **LIFT TRICK FOR AN OUTSIDE CORNER DROOP:**

All of the Eye MakeUp you apply (liner; lower lid, indentation and upper lid shadows; Mascara and EyeBrow color) should be applied upwards and outwards from the inner corner of the eye and stop short of the outer edge of the brow and the outer corner of the eye. Use a Kohl Rimmer under the eyes, ending with an upward line at the outer corner of the eye. Apply one coat of Mascara on all of the lashes; but apply three coats on the half-inch right above the center of the eye. Also make the indentation shadow line darker right above that thicker section of Mascara.

- **MAGIC FOR CLOSE-SET EYES:** Start by using a tweezing

trick—eliminating a small number of extra hairs from between your eyebrows. If redness occurs, wait before putting on the Eye MakeUp. Apply a pale highlighter from the inner corner of your eye, diagonally upwards from the base of the lashes to your eyebrows—covering the inner third of both lower and upper lids. Next, using your favorite deeper-colored EyeShadow, cover the remaining two-thirds of both lids. Extend this shadow slightly beyond the outer edge of the eyes and below the inner corner of the eye. EyeLiner is used from above the inner edge of the eyeball to the outer edge of the eyes, above the upper lashes and below the lower ones. Use two coats of Mascara above the EyeLiner, with a third coat on the lashes on the outer third of the eyes.

- **PRESTIDIGITATION OR ELONGATING A ROUND EYE:** To elongate a round *Orphan Annie* eye, you need to make it

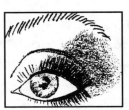

appear almond-shaped. This is done by using only one EyeShadow color—a dark, smoky shade—in a modified pie-wedge shape, with the point of the wedge just above the inner edge of your eyeball. The broader side of the shape extends from the outer tip of your eyebrow to a point on a line with the outer corner of your eye, right beneath the end of the brow. Run a narrow band of the shadow down and underneath your lower lashes, along the outer half of the eye. Eyeliner is placed underneath your lower lashes, from the center of the pupil to the outer corner of the eye. Use a dark, smoky color. Mascara should be placed only above and below the EyeLiner, leaving the lashes in the top third and the bottom half closest to the nose, without any Mascara at all. Put about three coats of Mascara on the lashes you do cover.

- **TRICKS FOR AN *UPPER EYELID WITH A HANGOVER:*** If you have

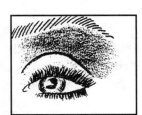

"bedroom eyes with a hangover" or eyelids that are beginning to age and droop, you need a quick change—and I have an easy one for you. A light color EyeShadow should be stroked and smudged all over the lower lid. Apply a dark EyeShadow from the indentation all the way up to your eyebrow, straight up from just about the inner corner of the upper lid to about 1/8th inch from the inner edge of the brow. The dark shadow on the upper lid should angle out to meet the outer end of the eyebrow. Apply three coats of Mascara on all of the lashes and if you have a really serious over-hang that needs camouflaging, get some individual false eyelashes to supplement your own lashes, applying them at the outer corners of the eye.

- **TRICKS TO OPEN UP NARROW EYELIDS:** The same medium colored EyeShadow should be used throughout this entire application, to give the illusion of more space between your lashes and your brows. Start at the inner corner of the eye and extend it on a diagonal, sweeping across both lower and upper eyelids. Use the same shadow to run a line the width of your lashes, underneath your 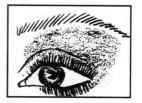 eye, from the outer edge of the iris to the outer corner of the eye. To draw focus away from the upper lid, apply a blue EyeLiner inside the lower lashes. Use a mid-range Mascara color. You should not curl your lashes.

♦ **SHADOW SETTING TRICK:** You'll need to use a spare blusher brush for this trick—a brush you do not use for applying color. Dip your special brush into some talcum powder and, after tapping it to dislodge loose particles, swipe it across the entire lids. The talc acts as a base to which your EyeShadow can cling and, since invariably some of the talc particles will adhere to your lashes, it'll do the same for your lashes. Once you've applied your Mascara, the talcum will also give the lashes some additional thickness.

ABOUT EYESHADOW COLORS

Here again, sit in front of the mirror and play with all of the EyeShadows you have in the house. Try all kinds of combinations, and don't forget to blend. Two, three, four or more. Layer them or stroke them alongside each other . . . horizontal lines, diagonal shapes, even vertical ones or a combination of any of them. Use complimentary colors. Use contrasting shades. Just remember the main purpose for using the EyeShadow is making your eyes look lovelier— larger, bluer, greener or what-have-you. Don't match your EyeShadow to your eye color. Using the same color as your own eyes over-shadows them, defeating the purpose of using EyeShadow to begin with. It's your eyes that should be noticed, not the EyeShadow. If an effect looks silly, laugh at yourself and move on to something else. Before too long, you'll have several looks that will please you. Those are the ones you'll want to practice applying and blending until you have them down pat. In case I haven't mentioned it—putting on your MakeUp should be fun. The results should please you, make you happy. While you might not get to the point where applying MakeUp replaces a good book or chatting with a friend, the results should be so pleasing that you look forward to your MakeUp sessions because you know the results will be worth it. I really want you to come up with your own color combinations. I know you can. Don't forget my earlier tip—light colors highlight or make an area look more prominent; dark colors minimize or appear to make the area recede. Now, to get you started, here are a few ideas:

FOR A NATURAL LOOK: Use soft apricot, peach, ivory or colors similar to your skin tones. Use nutmegy shades for a mysterious look. For example—use a soft beige on your lower lid; put peach or rose on the diagonal over the half of the upper lid closest to the inner corner of the eye. Ivory or another highlighting color, on the diagonal, across the outer half of the upper lid. Blend where the different colors overlap. Women of Color would select shades ranging from deep beige to a milk chocolate or bittersweet chocolate.

FOR THE '60s RETRO LOOK: Use pale colors, such as off-white or pearlized lavender on your lower lid. Draw a dark brown line on the indentation between the lower and upper lids. Use a mid-to-light brown on the upper lid, with an ivory highlighter at the outer edge and a dark liner right above the lashes. Remember to blend well.

SOMEWHERE OVER THE RAINBOW: Here's an unusual evening look you can use once you've become an EyeShadow Expert. Try a combination of golds or bronzes with aquas, blue-lavenders, roses, peach or pink, and burgundy or eggplant. First, use a dark liner, such as deep purple above your lashes. On the lower lid, in the area of the inner corner—use gold; near the outer corner of the eye—navy or dark mauve. In the indentation area at the center of the eye: rose at the inner edge; burgundy at the outer edge. And on the upper lid—peach at the inner; deep pink at the outer. Don't forget the blending.

♦ **SHIMMERY, GLIMMERY EYES:** Start with a black EyeLiner right above your upper lashes. Deep pearlized rose goes on the lower lid. At the inner eye above that, a pie wedge shape with the thick portion towards the nose in a frosty peach. Then sweep gold unto the upper lid, starting with an extremely narrow band at the inner edge, increasing to the width of the upper lid at the outer edge, bringing the gold down into the lower lid at the outer edge. CAUTION. Frosted EyeShadows can look harsh, especially if they're not blended well or if you have a great many age lines in the eye area. If frosty shadows are a favorite, use them—but tone them by using a light colored matte neutral shade brushed delicately over the entire frosted area.

- **FOR AN EXOTIC TOUCH:** Use blacks and grays with frosty pink. Smudge Kohl Rimmers around the eyes, very close to your lashes—more above the eye than below. Dark gray on the lower lid, shading into black at the outer corner. The upper lids are brushed with a deep frosted pink. Extend the colors to the side of the nose near the inner eye. Blending is especially important for this look.

- **SHADOW IN A HURRY:** No time to spend creating a beautiful eye? When you're finished applying your cheek color, blend some Powder Blusher from the center of the indentation, upwards and outwards, over the brow bone onto the outer section of the upper lid. Don't use anything on the lower lid.

- **WHEN IN DOUBT, CHECK IT OUT:** Here are some general suggestions for your consideration:

  - When you apply your EyeShadows, do it before you get dressed. In other words, it isn't necessary that your shadows match your clothes. If you've put on so much EyeShadow that it clashes with what you're wearing, take some off— EyeShadow, that is. You've put on too much!
  - At the beginning, when you don't quite know what you're doing shadow-wise, use muted colors and you can be sure you won't look ridiculous. Gray and taupe work for just about every one under 50. Over 50? Go for EyeShadows that are a little brighter.
  - Got baby blues? Use muted hues of purple, gray-green, smoky turquoise.
  - Green is the color of your eyes? Again, soft shades of violet, mossy greens, dark muted aquamarine and any EyeShadows with hints of gold in them.
  - You're a brown-eyed beauty—any smoky shade such as charcoal, olive or khaki, plum or aubergine.

- Hazel-eyed ladies have a choice of apricots, grays, olive greens and shades of gold or bronze.

- Should the skin of your upper lid have a yellowish cast, use a pale aquamarine EyeShadow beneath your favorite colors. This will offset the yellow and impart a clear, attractive look. Ruddy-looking lids need pale green underneath the EyeShadow selected to minimize the redness.

- Don't throw away leftover shadows. Mix them together—powders with powders, cremes with creme. You'll probably get some interesting shades. (If you end up with muddy colors——then you can throw them away. But, you could get lucky and come up with a real winner. Just remember what you mixed together, in case you want to re-create it.)

- If you haven't been able to camouflage the dark circles beneath your eyes entirely, do not put dark-colored shadow on your upper eyelids. The combination would give your eyes a hollow, sunken appearance. (It's a good look to use at Halloween if you're masquerading as a war orphan or some ghastly, ghostly ancient mummy.)

- Been in the sun lately wearing sunglasses? Then you'll appreciate this tip for camouflaging the no-tan lines left around your eyes and across the bridge of your nose. One way is to use a concealer that's a match with your suntan on the "white-out" area. Then use your Foundation as usual, blending well. Another way is to use the concealer you normally use to cover the entire "white-out" area. Cover that with a Foundation which matches your sun tan. Then brush on the *Adrien Arpel Real Silk Kaleidoscope Bronzing Powder.* EyeShadow fashions seem to change faster than other MakeUp fashions. The best way to keep up with them is to check your favorite fashion magazines to see what the models are wearing on their eyes. After observing these trends and trying to re-create the new eye fashions, you'll become quite proficient at changing your own look. If you don't want to be quite as *avant garde* as the models, cut out today's looks and save them for six months to a year. Then try them. That way, you'll have a new look when you get bored; but you won't be the first one in your neighborhood to try pumpkin leaf green or beefsteak tomato red on your upper lids.

Mascara—
The Quintessential Eye Product

Recently a writer asked me "Adrien, If you were stranded on a desert island, which three MakeUp products would you ask a 5,000 year old Genii to bring you?" Without a moment's hesitation, I told her "Mascara, Lipstick and UnderEye Concealer". If I'd been asked which one product would I want, without a doubt I would have selected my *Adrien Arpel Super Brush Conditioning Mascara* with its companion *Every Other Layer Lash Thickener, Conditioner & Separating Creme*. If the Genii balked, saying that I was wishing for two products, I'd just say, "They're always sold together. Just watch me on TV and you'll see, they're never offered without each other." Just my luck that it was a male Genii. A female Genii would know that these products are like "Love & Marriage"—they just naturally "go together".

It's funny that the word Mascara comes from the Spanish word for mask—"mascard"—because Mascara reveals the eyes in all their glory. It doesn't hide them, as a mask does. Of course, you can use Mascara correctively, to conceal flaws. But its primary purpose is to make the eyes look more lush, more beautiful by making lashes look thicker and darker.

Colored mascaras can be fun. Some experts say, "use brown Mascara for blondes; blue Mascara for women with blue eyes." Personally, I suggest black mascara or carbon (a combination of brown, black and gray) for virtually everyone. If you do decide to depart from basic black or carbon, test the color on your lashes, IN THE LIGHT OF DAY. Another way to use colored Mascara, such as purple blue or green, particularly for an evening special occasion look, is to make your first coat black or brown. Then dab your favorite colored Mascara only on the tips.

Many of you have asked questions about how to apply Mascara, how to make your lashes look thicker, how to avoid Mascara smudges. So, here are my tricks for goof-proof Mascara-ing:

* **Thick Lashes Are Easy As 1-2-3:** Without my Thickener, you can coat your lashes, upper and lower, on both sides with baby powder or face powder. Then apply the first coat of Mascara on top of the upper lashes. Let it dry and apply the first coat underneath the upper lashes. Let that dry. Now brush on the second coat of Mascara on the top side of the upper lashes. Let

that dry and . . . etcetera, etcetera etcetera. That's only with the first eye and the upper lashes. You'll have to repeat the process with the lower lashes and then move on to the other eye. On the other hand, with my nature-based *Every Other Layer Lash Thickener,* applied underneath the *Super Brush Conditioning Mascara*, you use the Thickener, followed by the Mascara. Continue alternating products until you achieve the length and thickness you want. After two or more double layers, you should have a glorious set of lashes.

- **TOP-OF-THE-EYE MASCARA:** Tilt your head down, tucking in your chin like a roosting bird and peer up into a wall mirror. Or, place your mirror on the table, look down and keep your eyes at half mast. Either way, roll the Mascara wand from the root of the lash, outwards, to apply the lash products. Repeat the process two or three times, allowing drying time between applications. The easiest way is to alternate eyes: first coat on the left eye; first coat on the right eye, and so on.

- **LOWER LASH MASCARA APPLICATION & SMUDGING:** Keep a Q-Tip moistened with eye MakeUp remover nearby when you use Mascara on your lower lashes to clean off the smudges. (It's handy to have for the uppers, too.) Tilt the chin upwards while applying Mascara on the lower lashes. Keep the wand in a vertical position and cover one lash at a time. If you have problems with the Mascara sliding off your lower lashes and end up with smudges under your eyes, you are not alone. It may be that your lower lashes, which are thinner than your upper lashes, are too thin to support the weight of the Mascara pigments. You can try applying a concealer on the lids and under the eyes, covered with a light coating of Powder, instead of with Foundation, before applying Mascara to your lower lashes. One trick: brush some baby powder on the top and bottom lashes with a spare EyeShadow brush. If these tips don't hold the smudging in line, your best bet is to omit the lowers from your Mascara regimen. You should also omit applying Mascara to your lower lashes if your have a severe case of under-eye bags.

- **TO CURL OR NOT TO CURL:** Unless your lashes grow straight downwards, you should curl your lashes. (With lashes that point to your toes, you'd be fighting Mother Nature; for trying to "fool her" she'd see that your lashes would break off anytime you tried to use a curler.) For us lucky ones—curling the lashes makes lashes look longer, giving our eyes a nice, wide-open appearance. The rule is: curl before you apply Mascara. Always curl clean lashes—the metal on the curler would stick to old, dried mascara, tending to pull out your lashes when you remove the curler.

- **YES, VIRGINIA, YOU MUST REMOVE YOUR MASCARA AT NIGHT:** I, too, would like to wear my Mascara 24 hours a day. But, it's absolutely not good for your skin or your lashes. Strong healthy lashes stay that way if you treat them properly. Leaving Mascara on at night can cause irritation and even result in swelling. Particles of Mascara can become dislodged and end up in your eye. Do this constantly and you'll be responsible for prematurely aging your eye area. Remove your Mascara every single night. *I REPEAT:* Remove your Mascara every single night. See the tips for glamor-eye-zing (somewhat) when necessary, at bedtime in the next section of this chapter: More About Eyes But Not About Eye MakeUp. (You didn't think I'd leave you totally defenseless, did you?)

- **MORE ABOUT MASCARA-REMOVING:** I would suggest—no, make that I would urge that you get my one-minute nature-based MakeUp melter—the *Adrien Arpel Coconut Cleanser.* It literally melts off your MakeUp. No more tugging. No more pulling. I've said it before—on TV, in my department store seminars, in my best-selling books—and I'll keep saying it.

YOU AGE YOUR SKIN IF YOU PULL IT AND TUG IT – DON'T DO IT

My *Coconut Cleanser* is not a fun product. It's a necessity. All you have to do is pat *Coconut Cleanser* all over your face, including over your closed eyes and on your Mascara. Leave it on for one minute so it can "melt" off your MakeUp. Wipe it off with a tissue or a moistened washcloth, using gentle strokes. Or, rinse everything off with lukewarm water. Your face will be squeaky clean and the product is not drying. My *Coconut Cleanser* is truly an example of modern cosmetic technology at its best.

Until you get my *Coconut Cleanser*, here are some other ways to remove MakeUp:

- Petroleum jelly—warm it until it's runny. Apply it with your fingertips; leave it in place, with your eyes closed for a few minutes. Then, with a moistened cotton ball, move the cotton downwards over your closed eyelids. Moving the cotton ball horizontally across the lashes can loosen the lashes and encourage lash fall-out.

- Use baby shampoo applied to a cotton ball or a Q-Tip. Dab it on your lashes and let it rest for 30 seconds or so. Then, use the same downwards stroke to remove the Mascara.

- Using the same method described above for petroleum jelly, apply any of the following oils: apricot kernel oil (especially good on dry or maturing skin), extra virgin olive oil or safflower oil, both good for all skin types.

Regardless of which product you use to remove your Mascara/Eye MakeUp, follow the steps listed below to minimize damaging the delicate areas around the eye:

1. Spread one of the products described in the preceding paragraphs all over your closed eyes, under your eyes, on the mascara-ed lashes, on the EyeBrows.

2. Count up to 50 before you touch the area—one-little-second, two-little-seconds . . . fifty-little seconds. One-Mississippi, Two-Mississippi also works. Just keep the product on for the full count.

3. Moisten a cotton ball and smooth it over your eye. Leave it for the count of ten and then, whisk it away, rapidly but gently. If you're out of cotton balls, rinse the area with lukewarm (body temperature) water.

4. Repeat Steps 1, 2 & 3 if all of the Mascara was not removed the first time. Repeat again, until all traces are removed.

UNDER NO CIRCUMSTANCES TUG AND RUB THE DELICATE AREAS AROUND YOUR EYES. BE AS GENTLE AS YOU WOULD BE WITH A BABY'S EYES.

More About Eyes –
But Not About Eye MakeUp

There are many tricks you can use to make your eyes look better that involve very little cosmetics or none at all. These are things I've discovered myself when I had a problem. Or, tricks that you, my loyal audience, have shared with me through the years. Many times you've brought a problem to my attention—something I hadn't considered or encountered. Your need and my knowledge were combined to arrive at a solution. So please, keep those questions and problems coming. Isn't there an old saying "Necessity is the mother of invention"?

Previously I mentioned that one of the times when MakeUp is a "No No" is when you're sleeping. Of course, there are times when we'd feel mighty naked in bed without a little something—such as with a new bed mate or one who was born a few years after we were born. Don't despair; Adrien's there. Your bedtime bag of tricks could include:

- *Creme Concealer,* applied lightly all around the eyes.
- *Real Silk Kaleidoscope Powder* brushed across the entire eye area.
- Some castor oil dabbed lightly onto your eyelashes instead of Mascara; then, curl your lashes.

You need to use a lubricating cream for the delicate areas around your eyes every night before you go to bed. Remember, there are very few oil-producing glands to be found in the vicinity of your eyes. To treat your eyes every night, I suggest you pat on my *Night Eye Gel* with its time-released ingredients, including liposomes. It's designed to penetrate and soften the eye area lines while you're sleeping. Another advantage: it's formulated so it won't slide around the eye area and end up leaking into your eyes.

By the way, in order to be able to apply eye MakeUp properly, you do have to be able to see what you're doing. Half of the time when you tell me, "I'm not very good at putting on my MakeUp," it's because your eyesight is not what it should be. Invest in a magnifying mirror so you can see what you're doing and you'll have very little trouble following my instructions for applying your MakeUp. And if you suddenly have problems after years of putting on cosmetics, check the calendar. Presbyopia hits all of us when we reach 40ish. Presbyopia is literally, the eldering of the eyes—the time when we all get a little far-sighted and our arms seem to get too short when we try to read a menu or a magazine. Many "reading" glasses are designed to double for MakeUp glasses. You just have to adjust the tilt of your head when putting on the MakeUp in the area of your eyes. Incidentally, if you've been near-sighted all of your life, putting on MakeUp will be much easier for you when you hit the 40s. You'll be able to see your features in the mirror without getting so close that you can't use pencils and brushes properly because they hit the mirror.

Another thing that happens when you're in the 35 and older category: puffy eyes. I know from personal experience how the water retained in the eye area can give you a shock the first time it appears! Some things you can do to de-puff:

- Get up extra early when you have an important appointment— at least 30 minutes earlier than usual—the extra time will let gravity give you an assist. The fluids accumulated overnight will descend and the surface around your eyes will gradually flatten out. Of course, if you could sleep sitting up the puffiness wouldn't develop at all.

- Pop a teaspoon in the freezer every night before you go to sleep. In the morning, place a handkerchief or some similar lightweight fabric across your closed eyes. Gently and slowly slide the ice cold spoon around the area of puffiness with the convex side towards your face.

- Since salt causes water retention, you'd be smart to use very little salt in your diet, especially after 12 Noon.

There comes a time when even the cleverest camouflaging tricks no longer conceal eye problems such as eyelids that hover over and almost hide your eyes or fatty deposits under your eyes. And suddenly, you start seeing ads for cosmetic surgery in a new light. There are a few things you'll want to consider if you're thinking about plastic surgery.

- You've heard that plastic surgery will make you look like you did on your wedding day—the first one—FORGET IT! Cosmetic surgery can give you a more youthful appearance. It *cannot* make you look like your daughter's younger sister.

- Cosmetic plastic surgery is *not* scar-less. Cuts leave scars; and, doctors cannot perform plastic surgery without cutting. Some good news though, scars on the face tend to heal better than scars formed elsewhere on the body. Also, with time, scars do seem to become less noticeable. Take a look at the scars you've acquired from cuts or incisions made elsewhere. If they healed well, the odds are that cosmetic surgery scars will heal well. If your scars are keloided—large, raised scars—any cosmetic surgery you have will probably result in keloids. Incidentally, the skin of Black women is more prone to keloids than is that of Caucasians and Orientals.

◆ If you have a history of yo-yo weight fluctuations, you should think twice and three times before having cosmetic surgery. Constant stretching and shrinking of skin is *not* compatible with plastic surgery. Another factor—if despite all warnings, you spend lots of time in the sun without protection, stay away from plastic surgeons.

◆ Once you've decided, "Yes, I am willing to make trade-offs to give my face a few year's of grace," find the very best plastic surgeon in your area. The skin around your eyes is very thin; it's loaded with tear ducts, glands, muscles, nerves. You definitely want a doctor who has had lots of experience in the field and knows exactly what he or she is doing. By the way, these procedures can be done as part of a facelift or alone.

Some of the most frequent allergic reactions involve the eyes. Many of these reactions could be averted by following some simple procedures or avoiding thoughtless handling of cosmetics. In general, because eyes are more sensitive, cosmetics for the eyes do not contain as many preservatives as other cosmetics. As a result, bacteria, mold and yeast growth is more prevalent in eye MakeUp. Here are some tips for you to follow:

◆ Replace your Mascara every few months. Every time you apply Mascara to your lashes, you pick up some bacteria. When you return the Mascara wand to its case, the bacteria travel along with the wand. Inside that dank, dark container, the germs thrive. The cycle is repeated whenever you use the Mascara. Do not add water to your Mascara—it encourages bacterial growth. Also, avoid pumping the Mascara wand up and down; it pushes air and bacteria into the tube, as well as causing the Mascara to dry out prematurely. Excess Mascara gets trapped on the "wiper" gasket on the top of the tube; then, when the wand is re-inserted, the seal isn't tight— which permits the Mascara to dry out. If your Mascara has any odor other than a slight aroma of hydrocarbon, trash it. Also, make sure your Mascara doesn't have a heavy fragrance. Fragrance is also a well-known allergen. Incidentally, perspiration does kill some bacteria; however there are no sweat glands on your eyelids. Guidelines for discarding eye MakeUp:

TYPE	DISCARD AFTER
MASCARA	3 MONTHS
CREME EYESHADOW	8-12 MONTHS
POWDER EYESHADOW	1-2 YEARS
EYELINER	6 MONTHS
BROW PENCIL/POWDER	1-2 YEARS
EYE CONCEALER	6 MONTHS

EXCEPTION: If your eyes have a tendency to be irritated easily, discard your eye MakeUp more frequently—every 3 or 4 months, to avoid the possibility of an allergic reaction.

- Share your clothes; share your transportation; share your recipes; but do not share your Mascara—or for that fact—your other eye MakeUp, with your friends. Incidentally, dry skin is irritated more easily than well-lubricated skin. As we get older our skin naturally gets drier. So if you suddenly find yourself with allergic eye reactions, it may not be the product or contamination. That's another reason for using my *24 Hour Eye Care Kit* (*Opal Day Eye Gel & Companion Night Eye Gel*). Sponges and brushes can also be the cause of eye irritation. They must be kept super clean and like eye MakeUp, should be replaced two or three times a year—more, if you're sensitive. To check it out, try applying your eye products with your fingertips for several days. If your irritation stops, use a new applicator immediately.

If you suspect that one of your products is causing your allergic reaction, but aren't sure which one, you can find out. Using cool water, moisten a small area on the skin inside your upper arm or your thigh; apply the first product that you use on your eyes every day. Check the area 24 hours later. If there's any degree of redness, you're allergic. If no irritation develops, wash the area thoroughly and repeat the procedure with the next eye product you use. If none of these products cause a reaction you can continue to use them. What could it be? Do you wear nail enamel? Go without for a few days. Your polish could be the cause of eye irritation, especially if you rub your eyes shortly after applying nail polish. If it's not the ingredients in the products, not the applicators and your products are new, you should see your eye doctor.

Are bloodshot eyes your problem? The best thing to do is find out what's causing the problem. When the tiny blood vessels in your eyes swell, your eyes will look bloodshot. The swelling can be caused by too little sleep, water from a chlorinated pool, allergies, too much alcohol or tobacco smoke, or eyestrain. Eliminate whichever of these is the cause and your redness will disappear. Should you have a need for an "immediate fix" because of an important appointment, you can use over-the-counter eye drops; but, only occasionally because these products contain antihistamines for itch reduction and vasoconstrictors for decreasing redness. If you start using them frequently, the time between separate incidents of bloodshot eyes may become shorter and shorter. There are saline solutions available commercially which will act like your own tears in reducing redness. These products can be used daily without any adverse effects or becoming habit-forming. In the event that you don't drink or smoke, have been getting enough sleep, and in general are living a sensible life, have your chronic red eyes looked at by an opthalmologist.

- Too many late nights, over-indulgence in alcohol on a regular basis, smoking—all of these will ultimately cause you to look older than you really are. Use eye gels, day and night. Wear sunglasses when you're outside, where squinting would occur because of the bright sunlight or due to snow, with its reflected light.

- The longer your lashes, the more you'll appreciate an eyelash curler. If you have very long lashes (lucky you), use the curler twice—once in the root area and once near the tips of the lashes. Apply your Mascara after you've curled your lashes.

I've spent a lot of time describing the many ways you can enhance your eyes. Take the time to learn how to make your eyes look great and everything else will be a piece of cake (without calories, naturally). William Shakespeare put it well in his play *Love's Labour's Lost*. When writing about women's eyes, he said:

> ". . . They are the books, the arts, the academes,
> That show, contain and nourish all the world."

With such a lyrical description, can we do less than make them look their best at all times?

FROM MY LIPS TO YOUR EARS

I'm sure Ogden Nash, American humorist, hadn't heard about me when he wrote in his poem, *The American Husband:*

"... He tells you when you've got on too much Lipstick,
And helps you with your girdle when your hips stick ..."

If he had met me, I'm sure he would have written it this way:

"He helps you with your girdle when your hips stick;
But Ms. Arpel's the one who knows 'bout Lipstick!"

As I mentioned in the section about Mascara, Lipstick is one of the three MakeUp products I wouldn't want to be without if I were stranded on a desert island. I've heard young women say that they feel weird when they wear color on their lips. Some mature women think they look younger when they walk around with the no-color lip look. Color on the lips, even if it is one of the newest pale shades, puts the last detail in place, when it comes to MakeUp. To me, it looks as if she's forgotten something, when a woman wears Foundation, Blusher, Concealers, EyeLiner, EyeBrows, Shadows and Mascara with bare lips. I'm sure you know what I mean. If you want to face the world with naked lips—fine; but then give your face a nude look, too. Apply some of my *Skin Correction Complex (Four-Cremes-In-One)*; use a bit of Concealer from my magic wand—*Adrien Arpel's Double Sided Eyestick*; and brush some of my *Kaleidoscope* all over your face, and let it go at that. But, if you're going all the way, MakeUp wise, then please, do use Lipstick. There's also a very practical reason for wearing something on your lips. There aren't any oil glands in the lips. So, even in the best of weather, let alone cold and windy weather, lips have a tendency to dry out, crack, peel and chap.

I've also heard you say that you don't wear Lipstick because it wears off too fast, the color transfers onto coffee cups and shirt collars, it feels too heavy, it bleeds, it breaks, it's too dark, it's too bright, my lips are too dry, my lips are too small, too big, crooked and on and on. I have a quick cure for all of these problems and more. Stick with me as I take you on a tour through the Land of Lipsticks and help you arrive at lip colors and textures that will make you look better and feel better.

LIP MAKING TOOLS

Listed below is a complete list of the type of products you'll need for a complete lip-making toolbox. You can get by with just the starred items; but, it certainly won't hurt you to know what it takes to be a Lip Master. Wasn't there a well-known advertising slogan a number of years ago "Try it. You'll like it!" Who knows? You just might end up liking the Lipstick Look.

μ   Pencil for outlining lips

μ   Lip Liner pencil sharpener, because you'll need a very sharp pencil

μ   Lip applicator brush, to fill in the lips between the outlines

μ   Lipsticks—in a range of colors (we'll discuss your choices later in the chapter)

◆   Lip stabilizer, to make sure the color you apply stays true—something like my *14K*

◆   Lip Gloss, because moist-looking lips are considered to be sexy

◆   Lip Peel to slough off dead skin on lines around the lips and chapped skin from the lips themselves

◆   *Lip Line Filler Creme*, a homogenized, freeze-dried protein used to fill in the "papercut" lines—the deeper they are, the older you are (I fill mine in first thing every morning!)

◆   *Lipstick Lock Pencil*, which is a flesh-toned outliner that prevents your Lipstick from running upwards into those "paper cut lines" (I can think of a few body parts I wish would defy gravity and would move upwards, can't you?)

WHAT NEXT, NOW THAT I HAVE THE TOOLS MS. LIP MAVEN?

Before we get into the problem-solving area, let's review the steps you'll need to follow, regardless of your LEQ (Lipstick Expertise Quotient).

1. Lip Liner: Make sure your lips are dry before you start to apply color to your lips. The pencil you use to outline your lips should be close in color to the Lipstick shade you plan to wear; it should however, be a bit darker. The pencilled line will *help* prevent lip color from

bleeding beyond the surface of the lips. Lip Liner pencils are generally of a consistency stiff enough to "hold the line". The older you get, the more products you'll need to keep the lip color where it belongs.

- The top lip—start in the center and, in one non-stop stroke, run the line to the corner of your mouth. Repeat, from the center of your lips to the other corner, in a single fluid motion, lining the other side. To make sure that both sides of your upper lip will be the same size, make an "X" starting from the highest points on either side of the center.

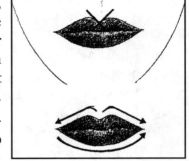

- The bottom lip—With one non-stop stroke, line the bottom lip from one corner to the other.

If the Lipstick you plan to wear is a very pale shade, you may want to consider applying a slightly darker Lipstick outline with a Lip Brush because Pencils, not always available in truly pale colors, could make the outline appear to be too hard-edged. You do need a bit more expertise to create an outline with a brush than with a pencil. It will take a little practice; but as my mother said about playing the piano—you'll soon be perfect if you practice. Fortunately, her advice translated well to the field of cosmetics. In the beginning, prop your elbows on the table or another solid surface to steady your hand.

2. An under-coating, applied with a brush, is next for women whose Lipstick has a tendency to turn color shortly after application. A product such as the *Adrien Arpel 14K Under Lipstick Color Stabilizer* will work wonders at making sure that the color on your lips stays the same as the color in your tube of Lipstick.

3. With your lip brush, fill in the surface of your lips. The top lip should be filled in half a lip at a time—from the center to the corners. This method helps somewhat in keeping your lip color from running uphill. The bottom lip is filled in by applying one band of color, from each corner towards the middle, right next to the pencilled outline. If you prefer, you can apply the Lipstick from corner to corner in one smooth stroke. Then, using parallel, horizontal strokes, fill in the rest of the lip's surface. By the way, stroke the lip brush lightly over

the Lipstick in one direction to pick up the color. Don't pick up globs of color by "boring" the brush into the Lipstick. You can also take a tip from the TV anchorwomen. You'll notice they present a soft and appealing look by wearing a little lighter shade on the top lip than on the bottom. Why not experiment a bit, yourself. Try one color. Try light on top; dark on bottom; and then try the opposite. You're probably wondering if you can put on your Lipstick right from the tube. Sure; but your finished lips will not look quite as nice nor last quite as long.

4. Unless you've decided that you want a two-toned look, use your brush to blend the Lip Liner and the Lipstick color. No demarcation line should be visible between the liner and the Lipstick.

SPECIAL LIPSTICK EFFECTS

Now that we've covered Art of Applying Lipstick 101, you may want to get into an advanced class. There are many tricks to make your lips looks prettier, moister, larger, smaller, fuller, more stylized. Let's explore a few of them together—camouflaging, priming, trying, styling and correcting. Lipsticks come in a stick or a cream. The basic formulas available are matte, frosted, regular, moisturized, long-lasting. There are no hard and fast rules in these areas. You'll have to experiment to find out what you like the best.

- **SEXY LIPS – TWO-WAYS:** The trick is to put a dab of something in the center of the bottom lip. It could be a lighter-colored frosted Lipstick, some gold powder, a dab of lip gloss, even a dot of petroleum jelly. Another way to a sexy mouth is to use pencil on the inner, center of your lower lip—a color darker than your own lip color and darker than the Lipstick you plan to wear on the balance of your lips.

- **LIPS WITH STAYING POWER:** To keep your lip colors on your lips for a long time try the following:
  1. Use a liquid Foundation instead of a cream. With a cream Foundation, the lip colors tend to slide all over the place. Let the Foundation set before you continue.
  2. Powder your lips so the Lipstick will have a surface to which it can adhere. Then, apply Lip Liner and Lipstick as described above.

The simplest way of all to keep your Lipstick where it belongs—on your lips—is to use my new *Lipstick Lock*. It won't come off on coffee cups, on your significant other's lips, cheeks or shirts. The easy way to get it off is to use its companion *Vanilla Bean Lip Cleanser*, leaving it on for one minute and then tissuing it off.

♦ **WHEN LIPSTICK WANDERS:** One of the most annoying problems with Lipsticks occurs once the skin right above the top of your upper lip starts to get those fine vertical lines, often called paper cut lines. You've heard me mention that Lipstick defies gravity and bleeds upwards into these tiny lines. Makes the most lush pair of lips look quite unattractive. Fortunately, I've come up with a number of ways to deal with the situation. I've listed them below, starting with tricks to handle this problem when the first faint traces of these lines appear and continue to solutions for the years when the problem is full blown.

1. In Stage One of lip lining, you should use a very sharp lip pencil to create a very well defined line. A firm, sharp point is absolutely essential; so sharpen between each using. Another way to keep your pencil firm is to keep it in the freezer between applications. Pull your lips taut by making a V-shape with your middle and forefinger on either side of your mouth. It's easier to paint and draw on a smooth surface.

2. Stage Two—usually about the time you hit the mid-forties. Run a Concealer stick lightly over the area right above the top edge of your upper lip, before you apply your Foundation. Then proceed as usual with a light application of Powder, Lip Liner and Lipstick. Reminder: use a liquid Foundation.

3. Stage Three. No doubt about it. You can see deepening lines all around the area of your lips—mostly on the top—but a few near the corners and underneath, too. Now *Adrien Arpel's Line Fill*, a clear, firm colorless paste comes to the rescue. Before you put on your Foundation, using the thinner applicator that comes with the *Line Fill*, spread it all over the entire area around your lips. While you're at it, use the thicker brush to do the deep nose-to-mouth lines and the downward lines which have most likely developed at the corners of your mouth. Apply your Foundation. If you can still see little crevices you know that next time you'll have to make two applications of *Line Fill*. The purpose of *Line Fill* is to fill the lines to the point that they are on a level with the surrounding surface. Putty does the same job for walls

when you're painting a room as Line Fill does for your face. It makes a smooth, even surface on which to paint your colors.

- **CORNERING:** Perfect Lipstick application requires paying special attention to the corners of your mouth. Open wide and say "OH". Using the narrow edge of your lip brush, pick up a small amount of color and, keeping your lips stretched, paint the corners. Although it's a bit more difficult to do, you can also corner your lips with a lip pencil.

- **LIP COLORING CHOICES:** First rule—if you think your mouth is too large, wear muted or dark shades to make it appear to be smaller. Conversely, if you think your mouth is too small, use brighter, lighter shades to make it seem larger. If you think your mouth is perfect, you can wear whatever color you want on your lips. By the way, you really don't have to choose a lip color to match an ouffit. It should be in the same color family but, not necessarily the identical color. Your Lipstick color should relate to your overall MakeUp, especially to your Blusher. Consider how a cherry red Lipstick would look with pale, barely there cheeks. Peculiar, to say the least.

From here on, there are no longer any hard and fast rules—just tips on choosing colors for your lips that are most flattering to you. If you're really into Eye MakeUp, you'll want a Lipstick that balances. Again, do some visualizing; imagine how a woman wearing dark charcoal and deep peach EyeShadows, charcoal EyeLiner or Rimmers and three layers of thickener and black Mascara would look if her lips were covered only with a colorless lip glosser. She'd look as if she'd been interrupted in the middle of putting on her MakeUp and didn't have a chance to finish.

What I'm really saying is that nowadays you can wear almost any color that pleases you, as long as you've considered the factors I mentioned above. When I was in my teens, redheads weren't supposed to wear pinks. Blondes were supposed to stay away from deep, luscious reds. Earth toned Lipsticks were still in the future and everyone's first Lipstick was a waxy orange-colored stick that turned into an almost invisible pale pink on the lips. Today regardless of your age, with a bit of common sense, you can have a Lipstick wardrobe. Or better yet, watch for one of my special kits with a whole range of lip colors that you can blend to suit your mood, whatever it is.

♦ **A STICK OF A DIFFERENT COLOR:** Like the Horse of a Different Color in *The Wizard of Oz*, there are Lipstick colors that can change color within ten minutes of the time they land on your lips. Your own body chemistry can be the culprit. Pollution can change your Lipstick. Look what it does to buildings. What you eat and drink, including water with its fluoridation—all can affect the color-trueness of your lip colors. What to do? I've already mentioned *Adrien Arpel 14K Under Lipstick Color Stabilizer*. As its name describes, it's worn underneath your usual shade if that has a tendency to turn color once it's on your mouth.

If you haven't had a chance to get my *14K*, try applying Foundation plus powder to your lips to make a barricade against the chemicals in your saliva which may be the internal cause of the Lipstick turning blue. Then apply your liner and Lipstick and finish off with a drop of lanolin, applied to your lips with a brush. This would be a guard against chemicals from the outside which come in contact with your mouth.

Of course, the simplest way to avoid lip color that turns color when you wear it, is to purchase Lipsticks that don't. Easier said than done. But, you could try this: put some of the Lipstick you're considering buying on your pinkie or your index finger (which are closer to the texture and color of your lips than the back of your hand is). Wander around the store for 10 to 15 minutes. If it doesn't change color, in all likelihood it will remain true when you apply it to your lips.

♦ **QUICK, SLICK TRICKS & TIPS:** Here are a things you can do in an instant to offset little annoyances that occur with Lipstick or around the mouth:

♦ Winter Lipstick too dark for Spring—try your *14K* or some lip gloss underneath to lighten the shade somewhat. Long enough 'til you can get a new one. (Any excuse will do to add a new Lipstick to your collection.)

♦ Like the look of gloss but *not* the feel? Put some Blush Powder in your favorite shade on your little finger. Spread a minute amount of petroleum jelly over the Powder and apply to your lips. Presto—shine without that sticky feeling. By the way, you should only be using a little bit of gloss. You're trying to make your lips look as if you've just licked them. If you've started getting those little lines above your lips, apply the gloss on the bottom lip only, so it can't run uphill!

♦ You can even make your own glosser. Take the remains of an old but favorite Lipstick, mash it and melt it over low heat with a little bit of petroleum jelly. Store it in a small lidded jar.

♦ Want to get the most out of your worn-down Lipsticks? At your local drugstore or five and dime store, pick up a plastic compartmentalized vitamin tray (like a small ice cube tray). With a popsicle stick or a dull-edged knife, pry out the leftover Lipstick from the bottom of the case—one color per compartment. Apply with a brush. Not only do you use up all of the lip color—you can customize your lip colors by blending a just-for-you shade.

♦ In the summertime, if your lip gloss seems to melt before you can get it on your lips—keep it in the fridge.

♦ Your new Lipstick broke? Slightly melt the bottom of the piece that broke off and the top of the stick left in the case with a long match or a lighter. Press both pieces together lightly, matching the break so it looks like it did originally. Seal the edge where they're re-attached, by flaming it. While the Lipstick is still soft, smooth the edges with a clean eye shadow brush. Pop the repaired tube in the refrigerator until it sets. Don't roll it up so far when you use it. Use a brush instead of applying it directly to your lips.

♦ If your Lipsticks often break, here's a trick to make them more stable. With a razor blade, cut off the top of the Lipstick on an angle.

♦ Want to wear some Lipstick in bed— even though I told you MakeUp in bed was a No-No? Outline and fill in your lips with a lip pencil. It will take a while to apply and won't be very creamy; but it will give you color that won't stain your sheets. You could put a little lip balm on top to eliminate the dry feeling you might get.

♦ By the way—if you do get a Lipstick stain on a washable fabric, scrape off as much as you can. Then, just before you pop it into the washing machine, rub petroleum jelly on the stain. As with any stain removal, test it first somewhere on the inside of the fabric. Leave Lipstick stains on non-washable fabrics for the dry-cleaner.

♦ How about a sexy, pouty model's lips for a change? Outline in a darker color and fill in the upper and bottom lips with the same color, *except for* the inner third of the bottom lip. Fill that center section in with a light shade from the same color family as the rest of the lips. Blend and then spotlight the lighter color with some gloss.

♦ If you end up buying a Lipstick that you find too dry—don't throw it way. (By now, I guess you gathered that I tend to be thrifty.) Each time, before you apply it, spread a small amount of lip gloss on the tip. Whether you use a brush or apply it directly from the tube, you'll have a moister look and feel.

♦ A quick touch-up on your lips is just about the only MakeUp you should apply in public. If you need a total repair, because the lip color is all worn off, head for the ladies lounge. Don't try to make a quick slick do when you know you need a complete re-do. You'll end up with botchy, splotchy looking lips. It's worth it to take the time to re-apply your mouth from scratch—Foundation, Powder, outlining and filling—because it will make your entire face look like new.

TIPS FOR DRY, CHAPPED LIPS

Putting Matte Lipstick on dry, cracked lips will give them an aged, old crone look. Unless you're auditioning for the role of one the witches in Macbeth's opening scene, don't do it. Use salves or chap-prevention sticks to keep your mouth moist and appealing. As I mentioned earlier, lips are *sans* oil glands and, as a result, are prone to chapping and drying out. Most Lipsticks contain emollients which offset this tendency. However, around home, many of us like to give our faces a rest and go bare. Wear a coating of petroleum jelly or gloss on your lips. If you're already chapped, apply an ointment before you go to sleep. For those of you who have neglected your lips, try this: Apply scads of lip balm, lanolin, vegetable shortening, olive oil or petroleum jelly on your lips and leave it on for about ten minutes. Use a soft, but textured wash cloth which you've moistened with hot water, to buff your lips until you've removed all of the chapped and flaking skin. Of course, the easiest way to do this is to follow the directions on the *Adrien Arpel Lip Peel*.

To help lips that are already chapped and to prevent rough lips, be sure you also put the *Adrien Arpel Skin Correction Complex Four-Cremes-in-One* on your lips while you're massaging it into your face and neck. Use the *Four-in-One* on the outside edges of your lips, too. The Alpha Hydroxy will help peel off the dead cells. Use it at night, before you go to bed, in the morning under your Foundation and during the day when you feel your skin getting dry. When you go out into the cold weather or are going skiing or ice skating, your lips need extra protection. A chap prevention stick containing aloe can be very helpful in forestalling chapping. Carry one with you so you can re-apply frequently.

CAMOUFLAGING TRICKS FOR PROBLEM LIPS

If Mother Nature or her friend Gene Pool, cheated you when it comes to the shape of your lips, my MakeUp Magic can help improve their appearance. Because cosmetic corrections in the area of your lips are very obvious, you will only be able to make minor corrections. The good news is that those minor corrections will most likely be enough to give your shapeless lips a nice curvy look or give a smaller appearance to overly large lips.

* **FILL HER UP — SOLUTION FOR THIN, NARROW LIPS:** Narrow lips tend to make a woman look very stern and  older. If that's not the look you want, grab your lip pencil and remember that dark colors make things look as if they are receding. Your Lipstick and your pencil should be similar colors. With a lining pencil no darker than the color of brick, make an outline slightly beyond your own lipline. Do not run your line into the corners of your mouth; this will make your lips appear to be wider. Blend thoroughly so that the original shape can't be seen clearly. Apply some gloss over the fullest area of your mouth.

* **DON'T YOU WISH FULL HIPS WERE AS EASY TO CAMOUFLAGE AS FULL LIPS:** There are two sleight-of-  hand tricks involved here. First to narrow the lips, draw in your liner inside your own bottom lip line. Then, to elongate your mouth, extend the lipline slightly beyond the corners on each side of the mouth. Now,

do the same with the upper lip, making sure the lines meet outside your own corners. You can wear dark shades, such as hues of mahogany, eggplant or bordeaux.

◆ **EVENING UP LOP-SIDED & MIS-MATCHED LIPS:**
There are three versions of these problems.

MISMATCHED LIPS

NARROW TOP LIP PAIRED UP WITH A VERY FULL BOTTOM LIP—

In this case, place the pencilled line on the lower lip just inside your own lip line. Leave the upper lip alone. You can also use a deeper shade on the lower lip and a lighter hue from the same family on the top lip. There should not be any dramatic difference in the two colors—after all, you're trying to achieve a look of balance.

FULL UPPER LIP WITH A THIN LOWER LIP—

not as common as the former; but still something you want to correct if it's your problem. Run the liner inside the natural line of the upper lip. You can either leave the bottom lip alone or make it a little fuller by running the lip pencil line just outside the natural lip line. Try both ways and see which you like best. You can also utilize two similar Lipstick colors. Of course, in this case, the darker hue is used on the top lip; the lighter shade goes on the bottom.

UNEVEN OR LOP-SIDED LIPS—

You'll use the same principles as above. If the left upper lip is lower than the right, pencil in a lip line slightly above your own lip on the left so that it matches the right. If there is a great discrepancy between both sides, you may have to reduce the higher side by putting the liner on the inside of your own lip line on the right. And visa versa, if the situation is reversed. Just remember that dark colors cause things to look smaller or further back; light colors make them look larger or further forward.

DROOPING CORNERS—

To eliminate the appearance of down-in-the-mouth lips, you'll need to extend the outline of your lower lip upwards—not too much. A color one shade deeper should be used on the bottom lip. Also, place a circle of a lighter or shinier color at the center of your upper lip, to draw the focus of attention from the down-turned corners.

- You can even use Lipstick to make teeth look whiter and less yellow. How? Use reds, plums or pinks and in comparison, your teeth will look whiter and brighter. Browns and apricot tones should not be worn because they play up yellow colors.

- Adults who are having dental treatments which require braces should be careful when wearing Lipstick. Your best bet is to use a product which doesn't come off your lips easily—something like my new *Lipstick Lock*.

SPEAKING OF TEETH AND LIPSTICK . . .

You can create the most perfect mouth with the tips and tricks I've shared with you. But, if your lips refuse to move when someone with a camera tells you to say "Cheese", you probably have a dental problem of one kind or another. I'm only going to address those issues which do not require a trip to the dentist.

There are many things you can do in the area of prevention. Many of what people refer to as "problems with teeth" are really problems relating to their gums. The older you get, the more necessary it is that you follow the recommendation "See your dentist twice a year." Problems with your gums are exacerbated quickly and waiting too long between dental visits can result in losing teeth.

MASSAGING YOUR GUMS: Something you can do every day to promote healthy gums. Wash your hands. With a moistened index finger, rub your gums in a gentle, yet firm circular motion.

TOOTH BRUSHES: Your brush should have soft bristles. Before brushing, run the bristles under water to soften them up again. You may also want to become a two-brush owner—one brush with a bent handle for reaching behind your lower front teeth and the back teeth, top and bottom. The second one, the standard brush, for the rest of your mouth. You should also use the tooth brush to brush your tongue and the roof of your mouth.

BRUSHING: If at all possible, brush your teeth after you eat, with an up and down motion, not from side to side. Use a rubber-capped dental tip, held at an angle, to trace a line along and slightly beneath the edge of your gums. You can use the rubber tip which is on the handle of some tooth brushes or a separate tool, which is available with replaceable rubber tips. And floss—between your teeth, with an up-and-down motion along each side of each tooth to scale off the plaque which ultimately forms tartar. This three-pronged in-between meals tooth-and-gum care regimen can go a long way towards preventing gingivitis.

WATER: Both your nutritionist and the dentist should tell you to drink at least three or four glasses of water a day. Water, which has been fluoridated helps protect your teeth. And water any way, keeps your internal systems flushed and healthy.

DENTAL MIRROR: A dental mirror is a handy device to ascertain that those difficult to reach back teeth are really clean.

TOOTHPASTES: The American people spend over one trillion dollars annually on toothpaste. Many dentists say that if you floss exactly as prescribed and brush your teeth with water you could do without toothpaste. But, if you're like most of us, you don't do everything regarding your teeth perfectly. To see how well you do in the brushing department as far as removing plaque is concerned, get yourself one of those "disclosure" kits from the pharmacy. You apply an organic solution to your teeth after you've just brushed them. The plaque that's left on your teeth and gum line will turn a bright red or some other flashy color. You'll be amazed at how much you've missed. Toothpaste provides that extra edge we need. It's the abrasive in the paste that scrubs the film of plaque off the surface of the teeth. The detergents in toothpaste facilitate removing the residue when you brush. In addition to fluorides, some pastes contain tartar-controlling chemicals which retard tartar buildup.

BAD BREATH: Most of the time following the steps listed below will keep your breath fresh-smelling. If they don't, it may be time to see your dentist.

1. Eat regularly. Bacteria can cause buildup on the tongue when you skip meals.

2. If you use a Water-Pik, make sure that you use the low pressure adjustment. With the higher water pressure, it's possible for particles of food to be pressured-pushed underneath the gums.

3. As mentioned previously, brush the roof of your mouth and your tongue when you brush your teeth, especially during your morning routine.

4. Don't leave food particles in your mouth between meals. Brush right after each meal. If you can't brush, at least rinse out your mouth. If you can't do that, drink water after the meal. Or, you can use a *stuzzicadente*, my favorite Italian word. (It means tooth pick.)

5. Peppermint tea is a natural breath freshener. So when you can't use mouthwash after a meal, try ordering mint tea. In general, drinking tea leaves your mouth fresher than drinking coffee does.

6. Ever notice the fresh parsley on the plate of the hamburger with raw onion special you ordered. It's there for more than decorative purposes. Fresh parsley is a very good breath-sweetener.

That about completes our tour of the lips and mouth. So now it's on to the last step in making up.

POWDER—THE FINAL STEP

When I talk about finishing your face with Powder I'm not referring to the heavy powdery look that until recently seemed to be our only option. The powdered old movie stars did have the right idea and, translated into today's world, a moisturizing *Kaleidoscope Powder* gives your face a glamorous finish like nothing else can. Everyone should finish off with "setting" Powder or for a sheerer look, replace Foundation with *Kaleidoscope*. If you already own Powder and want to make use of it, or if you're not quite ready to try my *Kaleidoscope Skin Brightening Powder*, here are some tips for you to follow:

SOME FACTS ABOUT POWDERS

The Powders which you're likely to encounter in your experience with MakeUp are: commercial powder, baby powder, talcum powder and cornstarch.

COMMERCIAL POWDERS: Both loose and pressed Powders are often talcum based Powders. Iron oxides, such as burnt sienna, ferric oxide and burnt umber, are used to add color. Mica or titanium provide the opacity needed.

BABY OR TALCUM POWDER: Talcum Powder is the primary ingredient in Baby Powder. As I mentioned before, talcum is granulated marble. Under a microscope, talcum looks like small flat plates. It slides easily across your skin and once applied, is almost invisible

CORNSTARCH: Cornstarch is made from flour—corn flour. Therefore, it is organic and very unlikely to cause any kind of skin irritation. It's colorless and odorless. Great in an emergency or if you tend to be allergic to chemical products.

Reminder: Keep your brushes and Powder puffs clean. For your brushes, use the solution described on Page 40 often. Powder puffs should be washed frequently to eliminate the bacteria they are prone to collect. Dishwashing liquid, especially a gentle formulation, works very well. Wash by hand, rinse very well and pop into the clothes drier. Your puffs will not only be clean but fluffy again.

HOW TO APPLY FACE POWDER

TO SET YOUR MAKEUP: Dip your flat-ended brush into the powder; then, tap it lightly to get rid of the excess. Brushing outwards from the center of the face, stroke lightly over the entire face.

TO ACHIEVE A SOFT GLOW: This is for women who like a matte finish but still want some shine. Apply your Powder as above. Then contrary to the old expression "Keep your powder dry*" you should moisten your Powder slightly. Either a plant sprayer containing mineral water or a barely damp cosmetic sponge can be used. With *Kaleidoscope*, this step would be obsolete because *Kaleidoscope* has a built-in glow.

TO ACHIEVE A MATTE FINISH: Use your loose or pressed Powder applied with a cotton ball or a powder puff. Press against your skin for better coverage that also lasts longer.

TO CAMOUFLAGE WITH POWDER: Inasmuch as shiny surfaces appear to be larger than matte surfaces of the same size, you can even use Powder to make minor corrections when you don't have time for "the real thing". For example, if you have a receding chin, powder the rest of your face; leave your chin unpowdered. Your nose is a bit too prominent? Powder your nose but leave your cheeks on the shiny side, and so on.

To Powder Up during the day: You can carry along loose powder in an empty spice container with those "sprinkle holes" in the sealer. Just shake a small quantity into the palm of your hand, dip in the brush and away you go. Incidentally, there are big fluffy brushes available with small-sized handles that fit nicely into an everyday (large) purse. Prefer to carry a pressed Powder compact in your purse but like to use loose Powder? With the handle of your Powder Brush, scratch a big "X" into the surface of the pressed powder to give you just enough "Loose" Powder for one application. Don't forget to tap off the excess before application.

To avoid Powder being trapped in facial lines: If you have this problem, you're probably applying too much Powder to begin with. Instead of dipping your Powder brush into the loose Powder, sprinkle a small amount into the palm of your hand; dip the brush into your palm, blowing off any excess before you apply it to your face. Golly, Go Lightly. If you're a pressed powder user and have this problem, you're most likely rubbing the Powder into your face. It should be patted or pressed onto the face.

To counter-act a Powder that turns orangey: Make a mixture of 1 part bicarbonate of soda and 2 parts of cornstarch. Brush a very light coating of this mixture onto your face before you apply your Powder. Although it can't be seen, the bicarbonate acts like the acid pH mantle on your skin and will keep your Powder from changing color.

Since I consider regular loose and pressed Powders to be old-fashioned, I hope you will try the *Adrien Arpel Real Silk Kaleidoscope Brightening Finish*. In addition to putting a fabulous finish on all of your MakeUp applications, it works on all skin colors, from Caucasian to Black to Oriental to Indian. *Kaleidoscope* has five shades pressed together in kaleidoscope fashion. Each color provides specific benefits:

- Lavender serves to even out the variety of tones of your skin
- The Earthy tones provide a warm glow

- Green tones offset your natural ruddy tones
- Rose tones add a healthy hue
- Pale gold imparts a soft sheen to the skin

No one color predominates. All you see is an elegant, sheer patina. All the colors together give off a sparkle like the facets of a diamond.

There's also an *Adrien Arpel Kaleidoscope Bronzing* formula, designed to look as if you spent time in the sun—the more you apply, the deeper your "tan". There are five tones featured in the bronzing *Kaleidoscope*, each geared to impart one aspect of a sun-kissed look: soft gold for warming; mahogany for luminescence; amber for sunnyness; copper for shimmers; and bronze for a summertime glow. This is the easy-to-use, easy way to achieve healthy color.

To apply either formulation, dip your largest Powder brush into the *Kaleidoscope* finisher, tap off any excess and, with a real flourish, stroke the brush over the entire surface of your face and neck. Your skin will take on a silky glow. It even works to restore the natural glow of youth if you apply it to clean skin, should you decide to spend a day without any other Base, Foundation or Powder products. Once you've tried it, you won't ever want to be without it. Watch for it on my show.

CHAPTER FOUR
HANDS, FEET & NAILS

Hands, more than any other part of the body, give away many things about you. And, not only to someone who reads palms. Sherlock Holmes was able to tell people's occupations, station in life and sometimes even their home towns from looking at hands. Okay— you say that Holmes was a fictional character. But, I'd wager to say he was based on a real live person. Or, have you ever heard a manicurist describe someone's medical problems and nutritional status merely by looking at her hands and nails? Physicians often can. People who read body language believe they can tell what people are thinking or how they are feeling just by observing their hands. Age is definitely revealed by hands—unless, of course you use one of the Adrien Arpel concealing products. And hands tend to age faster than other body parts because they are constantly exposed to water and other elements. It does takes a little bit of time and effort to keep them from revealing all and also looking their best.

Your hands, like your face, need a good scrubbing, vegetable peeling once in a while and moisturizing very often. You need to give your hands a facial. Let me help you establish a hand and nail routine that will keep your hands from being blabbermouths, at least as far as your age and your dishwashing habits are concerned.

* **DAILY:** Keep a hand and body creme or lotion, such as my *Skin Correction Hand & Body Treatment Creme* next to your sink. When you wash and dry your hands massage the creme into the skin on your hands. For your fingers, make a loose fist with one hand and massage each finger. Do the same with the other hand. Truly, your hands should be moisturized and massaged any time they come out of the water—from washing your hands to doing your lingerie to wetting your hands when you check the temperature of the water for misting your plants.

    If you wash a few dishes during the day, take the time to rub some creme into your hands before touching the water. Then pop them into rubber gloves. A few words about rubber gloves: 1) Replace them often; 2) Turn them inside out after use so they dry out; and 3) Expose them to sunlight frequently to eliminate any bacteria that form in the lining.

In the winter if you live in a cold climate or where heaters of any kind are used in the home or office, you must apply a hand and body creme before you leave the house and again when you return. And get into the habit of wearing gloves. Put a pair in the pockets of every jacket and coat you own. If they are handy, you'll wear them. There's no such thing as over-moisturizing when it comes to your hands. For example, in trying to avoid winter colds, you may be washing your hands more often, causing redness and dryness. Just moisturize more often. If your hands are already in a state of utter disaster, in addition to the above, every night until they're back in condition, apply a thick layer of hand creme and put on a pair of those lightweight cotton gloves you can pick up at the drug store.

In the summertime, please remember that your hands need moisture and sunscreen protection. Hopefully, you don't expose the skin on your face and body to the sun without covering up and applying protection. But, judging from many hands I see in my travels, quite a few women are forgetting that the hands are more exposed than other parts of the body and therefore need even more protection. Moisten your hands when you're going to be outdoors and select a sunscreen with an SPF of 15 for total protection. Using my *Four-in-One Hand & Body Creme* daily, with its Alpha Hydroxy, will keep your hands in great shape, including helping to lighten those liver spots that have nothing to do with the liver. You ask "What are those liver spots anyway?" They come with age and are the result of your heredity (genes) and the environment (the sun). Pure and simple, they are a discoloration of the skin. That's why the *Four-in-One Hand & Body Treatment Creme* works so well.

- **WEEKLY HAND CARE** (Week One & Week Two): Set aside fifteen minutes each week, to treat your hands the way they deserve to be treated.

  During Week One, use a mild peel, such as my *All-Over-Face Peel*. If your hands have heavy-duty roughening, use my *Blitz Peel* (if you've already purchased it), to slough off the top layers of dry, dead, patchy skin. In either case, apply all over the hands—top, bottom and along both edges. Let the Peel dry for several minutes. Then, with your fingertips, massage off the dried Peel along with the debris, using a firm circular motion, until the peeling action stops. You can also use the *Skin Activating Machine* from my *Skin*

Correction Kit for exfoliating your hands. Just attach the Sponge Head attachment and swirl off the buildup. Rinse with warm water. With sharp nippers, eliminate any hangnails, torn cuticles or other jagged skin around your nails. Don't cut the healthy cuticle.

On the alternating week (Week Two), use the *Adrien Arpel Flower Petal Scrub* for deep-pore cleansing of your hands. In this case you would not exfoliate the palms. Be sure however, to use the scrub all around your fingers, fingertips, cuticles and the back and sides of your hands. Massage for three minutes—by hand or with the Brush Head Attachment of the *Skin Activating Machine*. Then rinse with cool water. With sharp nippers, eliminate any hangnails, torn cuticles or other jagged skin around your nails. *Reminder: leave the healthy cuticle alone.*

After your Peel or Scrub, apply a cream or lotion, such as the *Skin Correction Complex Four-In-One Body Treatment Creme* and give your hands a relaxing, yet stimulating massage. Here also you can use your fingertips or the *Skin Activating Machine* with the Massage Head Attachment to help the Creme penetrate so it can nourish, moisturize and condition.

- **BI-WEEKLY:** Have a professional manicure or, if that's *not* in the picture, give yourself a manicure. (More about manicures and nails starting on page 109.)

- **MONTHLY:** You'll need between a half-hour and an hour for this one. I suggest you do it on a night when your significant other is out with the boys for the evening, on a business trip or another time when there's no chance that someone will interrupt your treatment. Before you start, warm a moist terry cloth hand towel, (in the dryer, in the micro wave or wrapped in aluminum foil, in the oven; set a timer so you don't forget about the towel). Also warm about two or three tablespoons of olive oil.

While these items are being heated, apply a rich creme, such as my *Skin Correction Body Creme* and massage it into your hands (and arms) for about ten minutes—rather longer than shorter. Then wrap up your hands and arms with the warmed towel and sit around doing nothing for ten minutes.

Next, you rinse off your hands with warm water, dry them lightly and massage the warm olive oil into your hands and arms. Massage for about three minutes. Then, wrap your arms and hands in paper towels and either put them into a plastic bag or wrap them in a clinging plastic wrap, to lock in the moisture and oil. Relax, close your eyes and think about what color nail polish you're going to wear on your beautiful hands. After ten minutes, unwind your hands, slather them with my *Four-in-One Hand & Body Treatment Creme*, slip on a pair of cotton gloves from the pharmacy and head for bed. By morning, your hands should look as if you've never done a day's work in your life. If I were you, I wouldn't schedule a gardening project or plan or cleaning the oven the morning after this treatment! Perhaps a rendezvous with Robert Redford or Harrison Ford?

- **EVERY-OTHER-MONTH TREAT:** Want to give your hands a real treat? Try a Paraffin Wax Treatment. It's easy and very effective. You'll need some paraffin wax, which can be found in a hardware store, some supermarkets or craft stores. Using a double boiler, melt the wax. Massage your hands lightly with a moisturizing cream. *Test the temperature of the melted wax before you apply it on the skin inside your wrist* (where you used to test the baby's bottle). With a clean 1" paint brush, paint the liquid wax onto your hands. After it hardens, peel it off in large chunks. Dirt and debris will be lifted off your hands, especially from your knuckles, cuticles and any lines in your skin. Rinse your hands in cool water. Your hands will be oh-so-soft and smooth.

- **ON SPECIAL OCCASIONS:** By "special occasions" I mean on your daughter's wedding day, dinner at the home of the "Big Boss", your 20th Class Reunion (or 30th or 40th). Of course, to me special occasions are also a picnic with my two wonderful grandchildren or conducting a seminar for 500 of my best customers. Anyway—whatever you consider to be a special occasion, your hands should look as good and get as much attention as the rest of you. On the assumption that you've been following the hand care routine I've laid out for you above, here's one more trick to keep your hands from revealing anything you don't want them to reveal. Massage a good creme such as my *Swiss Formula #12* or *Skin Correction Complex for Hands & Body* into your hands and fingers. Then apply a small amount of a powdery cream concealer, preferably my *Blemish & Spot Concealer*, all over the top of your hands and fingers, blending and smoothing. Don't get it onto your cuticles or nails. Let it set for a few minutes and it won't come off until you wash your hands with soap and water—not on your clothes nor on your dinner napkin. For an extra special effect, brush some of the *Adrien Arpel Kaleidoscope* across the tops of your hands. Perfection!

LET'S TALK ABOUT NAILS

Nails are one thing you can firm and shape and put into top-notch condition, easily and relatively fast. Wouldn't it be nice if we could get and keep our bodies in great shape with minimal effort. Of course, I've become such a health and fitness nut, that I really think I would run or bicycle every day anyway, just because I enjoy it even if I didn't need to, to keep the size 16 that's lurking inside me from ever popping out. What? You thought I was born liking salads with low-everything dressing instead of jumbo poppy seed bagels with heaps of cream cheese, and diet jello instead of Creme Brulee. No, my dears; I have to work at it, just like you do. Anyway, back to the finger nails.

First some background about nails. They have been a status symbol at least since the Ming Dynasty, where you just knew that anyone with long nails—woman or man—was wealthy, one of the idle rich. After all, how could a person with nails longer than two inches lift a finger to do any work. Impossible. Why do we have nails anyway? For a very practical reason—to protect the nail bed with its network of nerve endings, some of the most sensitive in our bodies. The nails are made of keratin AKA dead protein, the same substance which is found in your hair and the upper layers of your skin. There are three parts to your nail:

1. The nail plate—the part that gets polished.
2. The nail bed or matrix, located about one-fourth of an inch behind/underneath the cuticles. Nail production occurs here.
3. The nail fold which helps control the growth and health of the nails.

Nails grow at the rate of about 1/8th inch per month—somewhat faster in the summer; somewhat faster, the younger you are. The thumbnails grow the slowest and the middle finger grows the fastest. If you lost a nail, it would take six months to grow yourself a completely new one. Your basic care for non-problem nails is simple and starts with a healthy diet and cleanliness. Other than that you should

♦ Scrub them with a nail brush daily. In fact, why not keep a nail brush in the soap dish of your bathroom.

- Push the cuticles back gently, right after your bath or shower, when they're nice and soft.

- Nip hangnails in the bud with cuticle scissors or nippers.

- Use a buffered nail polish remover to help keep drying of the nail plate to a minimum.

DO-IT-YOURSELF-MANICURE

If you've never given yourself a manicure, like anything else, it will take some practice until you get it perfect. Although I have professional salon manicures these days, there was a time when I had to do all of my manicures myself. So I know it can be done. First of all assemble your implements and solutions: nail polish remover, emery boards, small glass bowl, a soft-bristled nail brush, some gentle dishwashing liquid (ala TV's Marge, the Manicurist), some cotton balls or absorbent cotton, orangewood stick, chemical cuticle remover, sharp professional cuticle nippers, a buffer (or a buffing kit), moisturizing lotion or creme, polish (base coat, color, protective top coat) and some Q-Tips. Set up under a good light, with a table and a comfortable chair. Make a little pillow out of a hand towel. Cover it with another hand towel, the excess fabric hanging over the front and the back of the pillow, to be used for drying the fingers and the hands. Place a bowl of sudsy water at the far edge of the pillow, your tools and implements along the right edge and your cremes, removers and polishes along the far left edge. (Reverse this setting if you're left-handed.) Take the phone off the hook or turn on the answering machine. Send your mate to the cellar for his own do-it-yourself project or off to watch a football game and if the kids are still at home, ship them off to a neighbor's house or to one of their friend's—depending on their age. (Tell your neighbor that you'll return the favor when she needs some peace and quiet.) Okay—now wash your hands thoroughly and you're ready to start.

1. Pour some buffered nail polish remover onto a cotton ball. Hold the ball over the first nail for 30 seconds and, pressing firmly, use a circular motion, to remove the old polish. Repeat for the other nine nails. With a clipper, trim off any nails that are too long or uneven.

2. File the tops of your nails with the rougher side of the emery board. The best shapes are oval or squared off with rounded

corners; do *not* create points. *Don't* angle the emery board sideways. File with a light touch, with one long smooth stroke in only one direction—towards your body is generally the easiest. *Don't* use the emery board like saw, rubbing it back and forth because that would exacerbate the nails' tendency to peel and split.

NOTE: FOR THE NEXT THREE STEPS, YOU'RE BETTER OFF COMPLETING ONE HAND BEFORE STARTING ON THE OTHER.

3. Soak the tips of one hand in warm sudsy water or a creamy hand lotion. (If you haven't given your hands a treatment recently, you can soak them in heated oil or cream instead of water.) The soaking has two purposes: it helps loosen any debris around or under the nails and, it softens the cuticle so you can manipulate it easily. After soaking for about five minutes use the scrub brush to clean your nails on the top and under the tips. With a nail file or your orangewood stick, remove any remaining debris from beneath your nail tips. Soak your hand for a few minutes more, dry, apply a moisturizer to your hands and the chemical cuticle remover all around each nail.

4. Push the cuticles back, GENTLY, with the orangewood stick wrapped in absorbent cotton. Remove only the hangnails or torn ends of the cuticle with the cuticle nippers. Cuticles are a protective barrier, preventing damaging materials from invading the area where the nails are "born". Use a cotton-wrapped orangewood stick dipped in remover to clean up any debris or creams left underneath the nail tips or along the sides of the nails.

5. Use a buffer or a chamois cloth (or if the nail surface has ridges, use the fine side of the emery board) to smooth the nail plate. Buff each nail firmly in one direction—20 to 30 strokes will do. If you are not planning to wear polish, get yourself some buffing paste and apply it before you start the buffing process. The paste will give your nails a lovely, healthy shine. Finish off with a warm water rinse and massage in some hand lotion like *Adrien Arpel's Swiss Formula #12* or *Skin Correction Complex Hand & Body Treatment Creme*. If you're *not* using polish, you're finished. By the way, the smoother the nail plate, the better your polish will adhere. Reminder: finish both hands before you continue to the next step.

6. To prevent the pigment in the nail polish from staining your nail bed, apply a base coat to each nail. The trick to a professional-looking polish is letting the first coat dry thoroughly before applying the next coat, etcetera, etcetera etcetera. (Shades of Yul Brynner.) Next, apply two coats of your favorite color. Fill your brush with polish—full but *not drippy*. Your goal is to use three strokes to cover your entire nail—one on each side along the cuticle, and one stroke up the center, from the base to the tip, covering the nail edge to help prevent chipping. With practice it will get easier and easier. Soon you'll have seamless nail polish on each fingernail. Let them dry about ten minutes before applying the top coat. The last coat, is meant to seal and protect.

7. When everything is perfectly dry, using a Q-Tip dipped into nail polish remover, clean the cuticles of any excess polish. A trick to tell if the polish is dry: touch the nail with the tip of your tongue. If you get any sharp taste, it's *not* dry. WAIT.

TIPS FOR KEEPING NAILS LOOKING TIP-TOP BETWEEN MANICURES

Once you've gone through the effort of making your hands and nails look great, you'll want to keep them looking that way between your Manicure and Hand Care sessions. Do the following things for 21 days. (Some people say it takes 28 days.) They'll become a habit; your hand and nail care will be simpler and you'll be able to point with pride.

- Remove the old polish and put on new polish every seven to ten days.

- Touch up polish chips as they occur.

- Nip off hangnails when you first see them. Don't tug, pull and tear them.

- Before you use your polish, roll the bottle around in your hands. Shaking causes air bubbles. Air bubbles cause lumpy, bumpy polish on the nails.

- Use a pen to dial the phone, a pencil to push the buttons.

- Press the Up or Down button for an elevator with the knuckle of your index finger.

- Get some one else to open the pop tops on your soda cans or use the tips of your fingers, *not the nails.*

- If you use a computer, flatten out your fingertips to hit the keys, unless your nail tips are wrapped.

- Wear rubber gloves when you wash dishes or when doing other messy cleaning jobs and use work gloves to putter in the garden.

- To maintain the even consistency of your nail polish, keep it in the refrigerator between uses. This also keeps the color true. About 15 to 20 minutes before you use it again, remove the polish from the fridge. Leave it standing up-side-down. Rotate it between your palms when you're ready to start applying polish.

I DREAM OF NAIL TIPS
THAT ARE OH SO LONG

Before you despair, there are things you can do to grow long nails, from wrapping them yourself to having one of a variety of sculptured-type nails professionally applied. First let me discuss nail wrapping. These methods are meant to strengthen your nails until you can grow them long.

VERY SHORT NAIL WRAPS: The harder your nails get, the better chance you have of growing them to dragon lady proportions. First, apply a coat of nail glue (with its "mystery" ingredient—*ethyl cyanocrylate*) onto the nail plate, making sure you don't glue the cuticles. Pop a small piece of toilet paper on top of the nail. Don't worry if it doesn't fit perfectly. Just make sure to steer clear of the cuticle. Apply another coat of nail glue on top of that and let it dry thoroughly. With the fine side of an emery board, buff the coated nail surface to smooth it, filing off any excess paper, while you're at it. Apply your base coat, two coats of polish and your top coat as usual, allowing plenty of time to dry.

WRAPS FOR NAILS WITH A LITTLE FREE EDGE: If your nails split, peel or flake but you have managed to grow them a little, this method is for you. You can use it when your nails are long enough so that when you hold up your hands, palms facing you, you can see the nail tips protruding slightly above the top of the fingers. What this method does is make your nail tips tough enough so they can grow longer. The supplies you'll need are:

- Single-ply toilet paper, the paper used for coffee filters, scraps of sheer silk or linen fabric—enough to make ten "caps", one for each nail.

- The liquid from a nail wrapping kit. These are available at the larger drug stores, five and dime variety stores and at beauty supply houses.

- Scissors, orangewood sticks and emery boards.

- Polishes: base, color, clear top coat.

Now you're ready. Just be forewarned that the first time you do this you may have more bumps than an Egyptian belly dancer. But again, with that oft-used word—**PRACTICE**—you'll be able to produce smooth coverings for your nails.

1. Cut your paper or fabric into 10 wedges—sized to cover your nails, with enough left at the top so you can tuck the paper/fabric

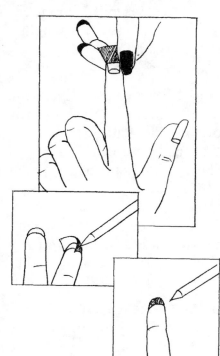

underneath the free edge. Line the wedges up in the same order as your fingernails. LEFT HAND: pinky, ring finger, middle finger, pointer, thumb; RIGHT HAND: thumb, pointer, middle finger, ring finger, pinky. (Do you feel like you're back in Kindergarten? That's Okay; you'll have long nails to show for it.)

2. One by one, as you get ready to apply one to a nail, soak the correctly sized paper/fabric wedge with the liquid from the nail kit.

3. Place the paper or fabric wedge on the tip and corners of the pinky, with the paper or fabric extending lightly over the free edge, all around the nail.

4. Make little cuts along the extended edge to facilitate the wrapping process.

5. With an orangewood stick, tuck the extended paper/fabric under the free edge, smoothing as you go. Dip the orangewood stick into nail polish remover to aid in removing lumps and bumps.

6. Repeat steps 3, 4 and 5 with the other nine nails.

7. If any of the capped nails still look lumpy when you're finished with Steps 2 through 5, use a buffer or the fine side of an emery board to complete the smoothing.

8. Apply one coat of a base coat. Make sure the underneath side of the free edge gets coated as well. When the first coat is dry, brush on two coats of colored polish, allowing in-between drying time. Your final coat should be a clear sealer.

9. These capped nails should last about two weeks. However, do brush on a thin coat of polish every night.

You do *not* have to remove these caps every two weeks and start from scratch. When you're ready for a "refresher", soak your finger caps in cool water to moisten them. Using the rough side of an emery board, file to smooth the paper/wedges where they meet the nail surface; then, re-wrap over the original wrap, following the 8 steps described above.

After several refresher nail cappings, you will have to start from the beginning unless you like the idea of walking around looking as if you're auditioning for the lead in *The Night the Mummies Danced*. Use one cotton ball soaked in nail polish remover, to get the old polish off each nail. Hold the saturated cotton on the nail for one to two minutes and then rotate it to remove the old polish. Next, soak your hands in warm, sudsy water. If there's any polish or wrap left, repeat the removal process. Before applying a new set of caps, give your hands a treatment such as described early in this chapter. But don't just cap them automatically. You may have grown your nails to a length you like. To keep them strong, try using a polish which contains fibers to keep the tips hard. If you notice that the peeling, cracking and flaking starts again, you'll have to wrap again.

BUT, I WANT LONG NAILS *RIGHT NOW*

Long nails instantly, or at least in an hour or so, are definitely a possibility. As with other forms of instant gratification, there's a price to pay, least of which is the price you have to pay to have them done.

There are nail tips, plastic nails and sculptured nails. Nail tips are usually the least expensive ($30 to $60 a set) and sculptured nails, the most expensive ($60 to $100 for ten perfect nails), with plastic nails being priced somewhere in between.

◆ **SCULPTURED PORCELAIN OR ACRYLIC NAILS:** Sculptured nails are made by applying a mixture of a powder, combined with a chemical that can be shaped and molded. This acrylic or porcelain mixture covers your own nail completely. Porcelain sculptured nails last longer; but when these break, they break to your natural nail. Acrylic nails are not as durable, are flammable, and do not stand up well to pressure. However your own nail is not damaged when an acrylic nail is broken. With both types, care must be taken so that your own nails can "breathe" by leaving a small space where the nail joins the cuticle. If this isn't done, it may cause disruption in the growth of your own nail. As your own nails grow, the sculptured nails will need "fill-ins" about every three weeks.

Sculptured nails provide women who absolutely can't seem to grow their own nails, with a hand and nail look of which they can be proud. Sculptured nails are a boon to nail-biters. And, if your hands are plump because you haven't yet gotten your act together to lose that weight you really want to lose, sculptured nails can make your hands look elegant and slim.

But, as I mentioned at the start of this section, there are negatives. Your own nails become softer than they usually are after you wear sculptured nails. If water becomes trapped between the sculptured nail and your own, discoloration occurs. You'll have to remove the sculptured nail and go without until the discoloration is gone. Some people are allergic to the chemicals used in applying the sculptured nails, and end up with redness, itching and/or swelling. There is the possibility of a fungal infection developing underneath your own nail. Sometimes, unattractive ridges will form on your own nails, which persist long after you've stopped wearing artificial nails.

If you have nails which are usually brittle or thin, don't have sculptured nails applied. If your nails or cuticles are injured in any way—do not use sculptured nails until your own are completely healed. Should you already have sculptured nails applied and the nails become discolored, lift or separate, have them removed immediately, preferably by a professional nail technician. If that's not possible, do it yourself. Soak your finger in nail polish remover. Next, using nail nippers or clippers, trim away the free edge of the sculptured nail. Now comes the more difficult part—you'll have to clip away little bits of the molded nail, being careful not to damage your own nail in the process. Keep on chipping at the acrylic or porcelain until you reach your own nail.

One other factor, long nails—your own or sculptured—are not easy to work with if you spend a lot of time cooking, at the computer, out in the garden or taking care of small children. Even everyday things like putting on your pantyhose, tearing open packets of sugar or sugar substitute for your coffee and hundreds of other small activities require new approaches. When you grow your nails long over a period of months, you make such adjustments so gradually that you hardly even notice them. Going from no nails to back-scratchers in two hours or less can leave you with weeks of ungraceful hand movements, with frequent nail breakage because you're just not used to those long things at the end of your fingers. Don't laugh—even going to the bathroom suddenly stops being easy!

♦ **NAIL TIPS:** Nail tips can be applied in a salon or you can do them yourself with comparatively little effort and practice.

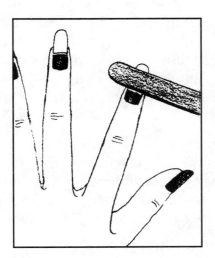

Purchase a basic tip kit in your local drug store, cosmetics emporium or beauty supply house. Your kit will contain nail tips of varying sizes. (If you're really into tips, you should keep some extras on hand. That way when you break or lose one, you'll have a replacement handy.) Select one appropriately sized tip for each nail and line them all up in the same order as your own nails. (Pinky to thumb and thumb to pinky—unless you're left-handed. Then, reverse the line-up.) Glue each tip to the top of the fingernail of the corresponding size, with 5-second nail glue. (Work fast because the glue dries quickly. Don't use too much of it, or you'll be stuck to your nails.) Glue a small piece of toilet or coffee filter paper behind the top of each plastic nail's free edge.

Once the glue has dried, using the finer side of an emery board, gently file the area where the plastic nail and your own meet, also filing the paper until it's even. When the surface is smooth, polish the way I described above. (One coat of base, two of color, one clear sealer.)

In case you're wondering what I do to have such nice, long nails . . . When I started out, I needed long nails in a hurry because I was asked to demonstrate my facials on a West Coast television show. Sculptured nails came to my rescue and my hands looked graceful and elegant as I applied my *Honey & Almond Scrub* on the face of a Lana Turner look-alike. Thereafter, for more than five years I sported acrylics. One day I decided I'd try the new wrapping techniques I'd heard about. I kind of liked the idea of having my own natural nails. It took a while; but with the long-nail wrapping techniques I talked about earlier, I was able to grow my own. Now I only use tips or extensions when I break a nail.

ODDS & ENDS ABOUT NAILS

• **SPLIT FIX:** Have a split nail—your own or a nail tip? Quick—get your nail glue and apply one (1) drop to the split. If it will make you feel more secure, you can also wrap the nail in the split area with a very small piece of toilet or coffee filter paper, nail glue it and when it's dry (in 5 seconds or less) buff slightly and reapply your polish on the top and underneath. To keep your splits smooth, moisten your fingertip with nail polish remover when you're doing your repair work and use it to smooth the surface of the nail.

• **H_2O ALERT:** Water is public enemy # 1 when it comes to nails of any kind, including artificial nails. Once you've invested time and money in tips or sculptured nails, lined rubber gloves should be chained to your sink. Because your hands will tend to perspire if your rubber gloves fit snugly, buy a size larger than you actually need.

• **GET YOUR PROTEIN DAILY:** Although gelatin, which is the wrong kind of protein, is not a guarantee to produce long nails for you, eating a protein-rich diet will promote healthy nails, in general.

◆ **GLUE SUBSTITUTE:** By the way, if you run out of nail glue, an effective product to use in the interim until you can get more, is clear nail polish.

◆ **CLEAR TIP:** If your nails are soft, keep them protected with a clear coat of polish. Re-apply one coat each day. After a week, remove the old polish with a buffered polish remover and start all over again.

◆ **EXTRA! EXTRA!:** To limit the breakage of your own nails, apply an extra coat of your base polish underneath the free edge. It will strengthen them.

◆ **QUICK CHANGE:** If you notice a quick change in your nails' appearance, check in with a doctor. What's happening with your nails may be indicative that something's out of kilter with your general health.

◆ **CAP TIP:** Ever have spilled nail polish seal your cap and bottle together so you couldn't open it? Turn the bottle upside down and stand it in nail polish remover, covering the cap for about a half hour. To prevent this from happening in the future, when you first purchase the polish, rub a small amount of petroleum jelly around the screw-top of the bottle. That should eliminate problems for the duration. If you spill polish in the cap or on the top of the bottle, clean it up immediately with some nail polish remover on a Q-Tip. Be sure to close your cap tightly because the chemicals in nail polish have a tendency to dry out or thicken.

◆ **QUICK SAFETY TIP:** Many nail products contain flammable chemicals such as acetone, acetate or toluene. Do not use open flames near nail polish, nail polish removers, acrylic nails (most flammable), liquids for repairing nails, nail glues, etc. Be careful. Back when I was wearing acrylic sculptured nails I almost set myself on fire while re-lighting the pilot on my stove. Just be very careful.

◆ **FILE THIS:** For the best and easiest results, make sure your nails are perfectly dry when you file them.

◆ **WHITE & BRIGHT:** To whiten and lighten the skin underneath your nail tips, cleanse with an orangewood stick wrapped in cotton which has been dipped into a 2% solution of hydrogen peroxide.

◆ **THIN OUT:** To thin out nail polish or base which has thickened, use a little polish thinner or nail polish remover. Add a few drops at a time and shake gently. Repeat if the polish is still too thick. Wait a few hours before using the polish, so that the bubbles formed while you were shaking the bottle, can dissipate.

♦ **". . . KEEP THE OLD":** To protect weak nails from even more damage, use your emery board to file your nails before you remove your old polish.

♦ **LEMON-AID:** If you have nicotine stains on your fingers, try a Lemon Aid to bleach the skin. Rub the pulp and rind from half a lemon all around the stained area. (Once you've bleached the skin back to normal, I wish you'd stop smoking. Then you can use your lemons for real lemonade!) Because citric acid is Nature's bleacher and astringent, you'll need to apply a moisturizing cream after you've used the lemon. By the way, using citrus products when you're heading into the sunshine is not a good idea because that combination can cause permanent mottling of the skin.

♦ **DRY, DRY, DRY YOUR NAILS:** Regardless of the quick-setting methods you use to hasten the drying of polish, it takes about four hours for four coats of polish (base, two color sealer) to dry so completely that nothing (but remover) will move them. There are a few things you can do so that you don't have to keep your hands totally immobile for that length of time. Plunging them into ice water (without the cubes, please) after the last coat has been on about 5 minutes, helps. The commercial fast-dry sprays make it possible to pick up your purse and slip on your jacket—but don't try putting on gloves yet or getting your keys from the bottom of your purse.

♦ **BASE-IC TIP:** Your nails seem to have a reddish stain. You ask "What's the problem?" Have you been applying a base coat before you apply a color to your nails? "No." There's your answer! To get rid of that stain, put some 20-volume peroxide on a cotton ball and hold it on the nail for about 20 seconds. Repeat, if necessary. To avoid such stains in the future, just use that base coat.

♦ **THE SHORT & LONG OF IT:** While long nails are great, don't go to extraordinary lengths. Too long and your hands look ridiculous. Too short; they look unkempt. You know they're too short when the free edge doesn't extend 1/4 inch beyond the ends of your fingertips. If law enforcement people try to arrest you for carrying ten concealed weapons, your nails are too long. Incidentally, most men really dislike very long nails on women.

- **HARD AS NAILS:** But, what do you do when your nails are not? Use a nail hardener? Some experts say "yes"; some say "no". Formaldehyde is one of the ingredients in hardeners. If you remember your high school biology class, you may recall that was what those frogs were preserved in. Formaldehyde can be an irritant, especially if you tend toward allergies. You might consider brushing white iodine onto your nails. It will also harden them, but without the negatives of a hardener with formaldehyde.

- **SQUARED UP:** Which is the best shape for my nails? Fingernail fashions change, just as clothing fashions do. The most natural-looking shape will probably serve you best, unless you've just been hired as a magazine cover model. A squared-up oval is always flattering and in style. Another advantage is that less nail is removed from the side, leaving it stronger and less prone to splits and breaks. Don't ever file in the corners of the nails. You'll weaken the structure of the nails if you do.

- **INKA-DINKA-DOO:** Got ink stains (or carbon) on your hands. The easiest way to removed them is with a toothbrush and a bit of toothpaste.

- **THE FRENCH WAY:** French tips—white polish at the tips and natural over the rest of the nail—have been in fashion for quite a few years, originally in the Thirties and then again from about 1985 through the present. This manicure is my favorite, as you may have noticed if you've watched my MakeUp demonstrations over the years on the *Regis & Kathy Lee Show*, where I am one of the "regular" beauty experts and have been, since the show started. If you want the universal look of a French Manicure, which will go with everything you wear, and you have a nice free edge, here's how to do it.

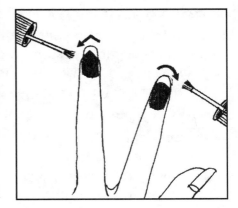

  - First a base coat is applied over the entire nail.

- White nail polish is applied to the nail tips, diagonally from the top towards the middle of the nail. Finish off with a rounded horizontal stroke. White Polish is also applied underneath each nail tip. Dry.

- Next, stroke flesh-colored polish all over the entire nail plate and underneath the free edge.

- When the natural coat is dry, use a clear sealer all over everything.

ALL ABOUT NAIL COLOR & COLOR REMOVERS

As lipstick is the finishing detail for the face, so nail color puts a finishing touch to hands and nails. As far as I'm concerned, if you've gone through all of the trouble to make and keep your hands and fingernails looking their best, you must at least buff your nails to a beautiful shine if you're *not* going to apply polish. It's *not* difficult to do. Just dab some buffing paste onto your nails. Buff each nail gently, but firmly, in the same direction for about 20 seconds. It's preferable to brush in only one direction.

With polish, however, your nails not only look fashionable; they have a degree of protection from everyday hazards. Polish is especially important if you want to grow your nails. If you're *not* used to wearing nail polish, start by wearing a base coat and a clear sealer. Then, gradually get into color, such as a pale pinkish-rose, apricot or a warm beige. If you're a novice, try to get a tone that blends in with your own skin color. Ready for more? Here are some tips.

- **ROSES ARE RED & SO ARE NAILS:** A true red can be worn by virtually anyone. Reds have been around since colored polish came onto the scene and are considered to be classic. Red nails even work for women who can't wear a true red on their lips because the hands are not in close proximity to the face.

- **TAN TONES:** If your skin has acquired a tan, there are lovely vibrant shades of nail polish you can wear. Consider bright coral, fluorescent pink, fuchsia and any of the frosty pastels. These are fun colors and are really not recommended for serious office wear. Of course, if your job is in a flashy field of endeavor where anything goes—brighten up with beautiful, bold shades. Incidentally, pearlized and frosted shades move in and out of fashion very quickly. So check with the fashion magazines to see what the models are wearing before you buy and apply.

- **NAIL DRAMA:** The more elegant your hands and nails are, the more dramatic the colors you can wear . . . burgundy, brown, maroon, near-black. If however your hands and nails are not up to snuff, you have large, bony knuckles or your hands are showing signs of age, stay away from these colors.

- **QUICK TIP FOR SHORTIES:** Nails and hands on the short, stubby side can also look quite nice with polish. You just have to be a little more selective. Stick with the natural or the lighter shades. To give the illusion that your nails are longer, center the polish on your nails, leaving a small space on each side without color.

- **SALLOW SKIN TONES:** If your hands are sallow or nicotine-stained, avoid polish with yellow tones—tans, apricots and corals—they'll make your hands look even more yellow. Stick with the rosy shades.

- **IT'S A MATCH:** I'm often asked whether or not lips and nails must match. Not necessarily; but, both colors should be in the same family. For example, you could wear coral nail polish with a peach color on the lips. Or, plum nails would work with pink shades of lipstick. By the way, I once read an article which indicated that men thought women were much sexier if their finger and toe nail polish matched. There was no mention however, of whether or not men felt the same when lips and fingernails were color-coordinated.

- **SPECIAL EFFECTS:** For casual parties or fun events, there are some things you can do to jazz up your nails, although I must admit I do think these ideas are more for the younger crowd. For a warm-weather picnic, paint tiny polka dots or stripes on your nails using a toothpick. For a holiday party, glitter or gold dust scattered onto wet polish, gives your nails sparkle plenty. Decals, pretty little beads can all be appliqued on one or more nails.

- **ON THE ROAD AGAIN:** When I travel for a week, I can't always pack clothes in the same color family and polish that's coordinated with a bright red suit will not work with a lovely fuchsia dress. My solution—I wear colors than are in the beige family, or as I said before, my "safe" wear-with-everything French Manicure.

- **REMOVER NOTES:** Because acetone, an ingredient in most removers, is drying, I would suggest you don't remove your polish more often than once a week or even, once every ten days. Or, look for a remover which lists *"butyl ethyl acetate"*. It's less drying than a remover with acetone. Another trick is to add a few drops of a virgin olive oil to your nail polish remover, providing you are not wearing acrylic nails. (Polish doesn't stick well to acrylic nails that have an oily surface.) As much as possible, keep the polish away from your cuticles.

- **SMUDGE REMOVAL:** While you're polishing your nails, keep Q-Tips and/or toothpicks wrapped with a little cotton handy. Both work well, when dipped in nail polish remover, to clean up the area around your nails or to even up the edges on the sides of the nail or in the cuticle areas.

Handy Extras

- **SOAP TO THE RESCUE:** When you have a dirty job on your list of things to do, pull out a bar of hand soap. Dig your nails into the soap or scratch your nails across the surface of the bar a few times. Because the soap becomes wedged under your nails, there's no room for the dirt. Simple and effective.

- **FINGER EXERCISES:** To be sure that your hands are not stiff and that they move gracefully, try these simple maneuvers: make a fist, open it and stretch your fingers as wide as you can. Fifteen times with each hand.

- **ANTI-GREENIES:** Have problems with your skin turning green under your rings and bracelets? Simply coat the under-side of your jewelry with clear nail polish.

A Bit About Elbows

"My elbows look like the hide of a rhinoceros. What can do to help them?" Let me tell you—you're not the only one with problem elbows.

I see rough elbows where ever I go. First of all, elbows need moisture as much, if not more than other parts of your body. So; every time you massage cream into your hands, save a little to rub into your elbows. If your elbows are really bad, massage them for at least five minutes every night with a cream rich in lanolin. To lighten the skin on your elbows, if it's darker than your arms, try this. Cut a large-sized lemon in half. Plunge each elbow into half of the lemon and rotate the elbow until it's surrounded by the pulp of the lemon. Stay that way for a good ten minutes. Rinse and apply a moisturizing cream. You could also use a grapefruit instead of a lemon.

Here's a step-by-step elbow treatment: wash your elbows thoroughly in very warm water. Scrub with a soapy brush or a loofah. Rinse and dry them off. Spread some *Adrien Arpel Blitz Peel* or another exfoliant peel all over and around your elbows. When the peel has dried, rub it off with your fingertips. Massage a generous amount of *Adrien Arpel Skin Correction Body Treatment Creme* into your elbows— gently and for at least 15 minutes. Repeat this last step twice a day until the skin on your elbows is soft and smooth. Then, massage in again, every night before you go to sleep. Without fail!

FACTS ABOUT FEET

Just because they're usually hidden in boots, shoes or slippers is no reason to neglect your feet. Just walking around on a normal day, the feet generally must absorb over 1,000 TONS of force. That's a lot of pressure. And, if you jog or run as I do, it's even more. On top of that, many people don't give their feet anywhere near the attention they need. Let's examine the feet a little more closely. There are 33 joints and 26 bones in each foot, some 125,000 sweat glands, veins, arteries, capillaries, blood cells, pores and thousands of nerve endings. Even without oil glands—and the feet have none—it's a crowded place, isn't it. You bet; over one-fourth of the bones in your body are stored in your feet. It's no wonder that somewhere around 75% of American women have problems of one kind or another with their feet. American families spend close to a half million dollars on non-prescription foot remedies. About 30 million Americans visit their podiatrist each year. What do they complain about? Read on.

Would you ever guess that the most prevalent skin disease is athlete's foot? (Bet you'd have guessed that it was acne. I did.) Incidentally, athlete's foot is something which you cannot pick up from the shower in the locker room, gym or health club. There are a number of yeast-like fungi that can infect the feet and cause athlete's foot. We all carry these fungi around with us most of the time. When we're run down or have been ill, there is a greater tendency for something like athlete's foot to erupt. But, you also need "ideal" conditions, such as can be found in an old pair of shoes or sneakers—a dark, moist and warm spot. The area between the toes, under the foot and the toe nails become infected with symptoms such as scaling, cracking, redness and blistering. Although you can do much to prevent athlete's foot (see below), once you've got it, you really should see a doctor for treatment. He or she can decide if you need a prescription for pills, some medicated ointment or if some other fungicide is indicated.

The secret to preventing athlete's foot is dryness. Dry your feet extremely well after each shower or bath. If your feet perspire air them out until they are dry. Especially take care to dry between the toes. Take your sneakers off as soon as you finish your sports activity. 100% white cotton socks are best because cotton permits air to pass more easily through the weave. White, because some dyes, when combined with perspiration can cause problems. When possible, wear footwear which permits the air to flow through—sandals, open-toe, sling back shoes, woven leather shoes.

AND THEN THERE ARE CORNS! What are they? Growths, painful ones, usually appearing on the little toe or its neighbor. Most of the time, but not always, corns are caused by wearing footwear which squashes the toes, either because of an incorrect size or an unbalanced last. What occurs is—the blood cells become dilated and cause a buildup of skin cells. The cells become hard and impacted and *voila*, a corn. When these impacted cells establish themselves around a nerve, it hurts—a heckuva lot. A podiatrist will "shave" the corns to alleviate the problem. But, how does one eliminate corns permanently. By eliminating the cause. Get shoes of the proper size. If the structure of your foot is not in balance, you'll need to see an expert who'll help you obtain mechanical devices or othotics which will change the foot's position so the weight is re-distributed. (Othotics are the cut-to-measure plastic inserts which are slipped into your shoes.)

HOW ABOUT BUNIONS? They are usually inherited and, if they bother you enough, you should consider bunion surgery. I'm told that you might be able to circumvent heredity as far as bunions are concerned by doing the following exercise faithfully every day. While you're seated in the tub, hold your foot with one hand. With the other hand, pull your big toe away from your foot and gently rotate it. Do the same with the other foot. It has to be an every day thing though.

WHAT ABOUT CALLUSES? Calluses usually appear on the bottom of your feet, along the side of the big toes or on your heels. Pressure causes calluses. When they first appear, you can probably get rid of them with a pumice stone. But unless you find the cause, you'll just get another one and another and another, ad nauseam. Carrying too much weight can cause calluses, as can wearing high heeled shoes which, because they cause the foot to slant, create undue pressure on the ball of the foot. If you can't determine what's triggering your calluses, talk to your podiatrist. A thin layer of callus serves to protect softer tissue beneath. Cutting away callus is not recommended, unless it's done by your foot doctor.

A WORD IN DEFENSE OF HIGH-HEELED SHOES. Some high heels can be good for some feet. Pain in the arch of the foot can sometimes be alleviated by wearing a heel which takes the pressure from the arch and puts it on the ball of the foot. High heels don't mean 4" spikes. High heels mean no higher than 2-1/2" heels. In fact, some podiatrists say that the best thing to do, heel-wise is to vary the height from day to day. This variation exercises your calves and Achilles' tendons by stretching them. If you're addicted to shoes with heels higher than 2-1/2" there's nothing I can say that will get you to change your mind or your mode. Here are some ways to offset, to a degree, the shortening of the hamstring muscles (they're right behind the calf), which comes as a result of wearing high heels.

Place your feet 36" (the distance from the tip of your nose to your fingertips when your arms are stretched to the side) away from the wall. Stretching your arms high above your head, lean forward and place your palms against the wall. Do ten push-offs, holding for a count of 15 each time. Stand farther away from the wall if you don't feel any pulling in your calves. This exercise must be done daily.

FOOT CARE BASICS

At the start of this section, you read about how much work your poor feet do every day. It behooves you to take good care of them. They like to be soft and look well-groomed. Honestly. Start by getting a pumice stone. Then every day, when you take your shower or bath, use the moistened pumice stone to remove dead skin. Give yourself or have a pedicure at least once every month to six weeks; more often in the summertime. In between use a clipper to keep your toe nails trimmed, cutting straight across. If you don't take baths, soak them once or twice a week, for ten minutes or so. Then dry them and cream them well. Foot massage is a pampering, luxurious experience. If your significant other isn't available or in the mood to treat your tootsies to a foot rub, just do-it-yourself. Not only will it relieve your feet, it will soothe you overall.

* Soak your feet in warm, soapy water—10 minutes, please. Salt added to the water will help in the exfoliation process.

* Dry your feet well and apply powder or cornstarch.

* While sitting on the floor, place one leg at rest on the opposite thigh.

* With your thumb, apply 3-seconds of pressure to the footpad, right under the big toe. In succession, move your thumb to the footpad underneath each toe. Apply pressure and hold for three seconds.

* Move your thumb to the spot below the big toe's footpad (where you first applied pressure) and repeat the process all the way across the foot.

* When you've finished the entire sole, before you go on to your other foot, take your toes, one at a time, between your thumb and your index and middle fingers and pressure-massage your way up each toe.

* Repeat all of these steps on your other foot.

* Apply warm olive oil or a nourishing cream all over your feet and put on a pair of white, cotton socks. Go to bed, relax and have pleasant dreams.

ODOR-BEATERS

Just as keeping feet dry is essential to beating the athlete's foot virus, so are dry feet the goal in eliminating the bacteria which cause foot odor. Would you believe that the sole of your foot can house something like six trillion bacteria. And, dry feet are the remedy that combats all of them.

♦   Change foot gear often. If you have a tendency to foot perspiration change your socks/stockings as often as twice and three times a day. As mentioned before, if you can wear socks, 100% cotton ones are best. Change your shoes at least once during the day if at all possible.

♦   Don't wear the same pair of shoes two days in a row. Let them air out at least 24 hours before putting them on again.

♦   Remember those 250,000 sweat glands in both feet, combined. They need an antiperspirant if your feet have odor problems. Check the ingredients for *aluminum chlorhydrate* which partially blocks the action of the sweat glands and ducts.

Odds & Ends About Feet

Ever wonder why it was a slipper that Cinderella lost? As far as I know, it's the only fairy tale written about the feet. I was going to say that there probably weren't even any standard tales about feet; but then I remembered *The Horse's Mouth*, in which Sir Alec Guiness plays an artist who spends his life creating huge murals containing feet. (Great movie, if you haven't ever seen it.) And then there's the poignant, *My Left Foot*. The phrase "standing on your own two feet" has come to mean being independent. In our system of measurement, 12" is said to have been the length of a British monarch's foot and supposedly, that's why we have a "ruler". Fancy footwork counts a lot if you're a champion figure skater. And, feet follow us to the grave when we're "six feet under". Before we leave the subject, I'd like to share some tips and foot-saving ideas with you.

♦   Going barefoot on grass, sand or a similar surface is a good exercise for your feet as well as for your legs.

♦   Sneakers shouldn't be worn day-in and day-out. But, when you do wear them, make sure they fit properly. And air them out in-between use.

♦   It's smarter to buy your shoes and sneakers in the afternoon because your feet do swell somewhat during the day. Buy them in the morning and by dinnertime they may be too snug. Same thing can happen when you buy shoes in air-conditioned surroundings; a cold climate tends to contract everything, even feet. So test them when you get home, walking on a carpet (or covering them with heavy socks to prevent the soles from scuffing) for a half-hour or so. That way you can take them back if they don't fit properly.

- Too much salt in your diet can cause water retention and swollen ankles. Cutting off your circulation by crossing your legs and hooking your feet around the legs of a chair can also cause swelling. Get into the habit of sitting with your feet in front of you, placed firmly on the floor. If you tend towards swollen ankles and legs, and you like to wear boots, get the kind with zippers. That way, you can unzip them periodically during the day to keep your circulation on the move.

CHAPTER FIVE
BATH & BODY

In most homes, baths as a luxurious experience have all but disappeared. Only about 10% of women take baths regularly. Another 5% alternate between baths and showers. The rest, because of time constraints choose the shower as their preferred daily mode of washing. In some areas, especially in the Sunbelt States, hot tubs are the only reminders of the exalted position baths once held among ancient Egyptians, Syrians and Romans. During those days, in Rome alone, there were nearly 1,000 public baths. People had "bath servants". There were cold baths called frigidaria; there was a bath exclusively for hot water, a calderium; and a tepedarium, for tepid water. There were special bath oils, special tools, special vases and jars—all just for the baths. Today one can see ruins of Roman baths in such diverse cities as Cairo, Rome, an appropriately named English City—Bath, as well as the German resort and casino city of Baden-Baden. Incidentally, *baden* is the German word for "bathe".

During medieval times, things that smacked of the Holy Roman Empire vanished. Bathing became non-existent—once or year or less. During the Renaissance, people became more enlightened and immersing the body in water for the purpose of washing, occurred more frequently—perhaps once a month. Even in the first half of the 20th Century baths or showers were relegated to Saturday night. Nowadays, thank goodness, showers and baths are a daily and in some cases, a twice daily event, even if they are not a two or three hour production as they were in the beginning.

BASIC BATH STEPS

Anytime you have 15 minutes for your bathing ritual, try this relatively quick skin-softening bath.

1. Run a tub full of warm water.
2. Add several caps full of body oil or add a teaspoon of your favorite cologne to 1/4 cup of baby or olive oil and swirl into your bath water.
3. Soak for 10-15 minutes; as you stand up, rub the bath water with its oils, over your skin.

4. Start your rinse with warm water and gradually turn it cool. If your skin is very dry and you haven't worked up a sweat, you can even skip the rinse.

5. Apply your body moisturizer after you've dripped dry for a minute or two, but before you towel dry.

LUXURY BATHS

I'm one of those 85% of women who rely on daily showers. But, I do try to make time for a glamorous bath once or twice a week, complete with bath oils, herbs and fragrance. It's truly a sensuous feeling and if I ever retire, I am going to institute a daily bath for myself. If you have the time, by all means, consider treating yourself to baths often. Baths can be relaxing or invigorating, stress-removing, designed to ease aches and pains or geared to cooling off hot or irritated skin. If you use herbs, tie them into a small make-shift muslin bag so the petals and leaves don't end up clogging your plumbing — a sort of bouquet garni for the bath. Essential oils do not dissolve in water; you'll need to swirl them throughout your bath-water so the tiny droplets cling to your skin. You'll also want a loofah in the tub and for when you get out, some extra large bath towels and a moisturizing body cream, such as the *Adrien Arpel Skin Correction Body Treatment Creme with Alpha Hydroxy*. Now you're ready.

RELAXING BATH
Herbs: Lavender & Chamomile
Essential Oils: Sandalwood, Mandarin & Lavender

BATH REFRESHER
Herbs: Rosemary & Mint
Essential Oils: Juniper, Lemon, Rosemary & Mint

ANTI-STRESS BATH
Herbs: Jasmine & Rose Petals
Essential Oils: Rose or Rosewood

TO RELIEVE ACHES
Herbs: Lavender
Essential Oils: Lavender & Neroli

SUMMER COOLER
Essential Oils: Geranium & Lemon

ITCH SOOTHER

Herbs: Sage & Basil; you can also add a 1/4 cup apple cider vinegar
if its a sunburn itch

Essential Oils: Clary Sage & Neroli

The essential oils and herbs can be picked up in most health food stores. Often small boutiques which carry items like potpourri also feature floral herbs and the most popular essential oils.

The temperature of the bath water should not be too hot. Very hot water is very enervating, dries out the skin and can cause vascular "spider lines" in your legs. Your best bath is a 20-minute warm water bath. By warm, I mean like a baby's bath somewhere between 95°F and 100°F. If your skin is very dry don't soak too long and don't take bubble baths, because they're even more drying. If you're particularly fond of bubble baths, try this shower substitute: use your favorite scented shampoo as a body wash, rubbing it all over. Actually, for the dry skinned body, showers would be the better choice.

BODY SLOUGHING IDEAS

One way to keep your body looking younger and smoother is to slough off the dead skin cells on a regular basis. Step into the tub and slather a sloughing cream all over your body, excluding the breasts and the genitals. Massage your body, using a thick washcloth, soaked in warm water. Pay special attention to the buttocks, shoulders, legs and knees, upper arms and elbows. Then rinse with warm to cool water. Before you towel dry, massage in a body cream like my *Skin Correction Body Treatment Creme with Alpha Hydroxy.*

Another way of ridding your body of dead cells and debris, is to coat it with warmed oil before you enter the bath tub.

For oily skin use sunflower, corn or baby oil

For dry skin, apply olive or almond oil

For normal skin massage in sesame, canola or walnut oil

Soak in warm water for 15 to 20 minutes. Then, using a plastic or rubber spatula, gently scrape off the dead cells. (Another sloughing material is a mixture of equal parts Epsom salts and table salt.) Either way, finish off with a final rinse of cool water and apply body creme before you towel dry to seal in moisture.

If you really want to give yourself a very special treat-treatment, try the recipe listed below after your shower.

TEXTURIZED PASTE FOR BODY MASSAGE
(2 applications - for all skin types)

2 Tablespoons Apricot Kernel Oil
3 Tablespoons Sweet Almond Oil
3 Tablespoons Oatmeal Flakes
2 Teaspoons Ground Almonds
1 Teaspoon Ground Lemon Peel
1 Teaspoon Ground Orange Peel
1/2 Teaspoon Apple Pie Seasoning
1 Teaspoon of Fragrant Crushed Dried Petals such as Apple
    Blossom Rose, Carnation, Honey Suckle, Freesia, Peach
    Blossom
6 Drops Neroli or Mandarin Oil
4 Drops Jasmine or Ylang-Ylang Oil

Mix the ingredients together, stirring and pressing with a fork, as you would when you're preparing a from-scratch pie crust, to form a paste. If it's too moist, add pinch by pinch the ground almonds or the oatmeal flakes, until the paste is easy to spread. Should it be too dry, add a few more drops of Apricot Kernel Oil, until the paste is spreadable. If you don't use it right away, label and store it in an earthenware jar, in dark, cool place.

APPLICATION: Take a relaxing bath or shower. Towel dry, lightly. Using small amounts, spread a thin layer of the mixture all over your body, with a firm, rolling motion. When you're all covered, use a soft, dry washcloth or a clean blush brush to remove the mixture, which by now should be powdery. If you'd rather, you can take a tepid shower and pat yourself dry.

MORE BATH & BODY CARE IDEAS

* **LOOFAH LAUNDRY:** When your loofah gets grundgy, you can just pop it into the washing machine with your white wash. Or, soak it overnight in an apple cider/water mix—2 to 1. Rinse it thoroughly with cold water.

- **HARD-WATER PROBLEMS?:** To soften hard water, toss a 1/2 cup of bath salts into the tub. A 1/2 cup of baking soda swirled into your bath water, while not as fragrant works just as well.

- **KEEPING COOL:** If your prone to night sweats, dust your sheets lightly with a baby powder or a fragrant bath powder. You'll wake up well-refreshed.

- **TOWEL RUB-DOWN:** A rubdown with a scented towel is a quick treat for your body. Just spray your favorite fragrance on a bath towel which has been heated in the clothes dryer. Rub the towel all over your body to feel great.

- **BUT I LOVE HOT BATHS:** You know hot baths are not that good for you; but you hate to give up the pre-bed sleepiness they create. Be a cheater, with my sanction. About five minutes before you're ready to jump into the tub, run the hot water with the drain open and the shower curtain or shower doors closed. As soon as the tub enclosure is filled with steam, turn the water to luke warm and climb in. It's called having your cake and eating it, too. I'm always delighted when I can come up with a way to do that. You too?

- **ALTERNATE BODY WASH:** If you love the way your shampoo smells, here's a way to expand its use. Pour some of your favorite shampoo into a bath mitt. Add a little water to dilute it and lather it all over your body. Mmmm.

- **POWDER ME DRY:** To keep your cool when others around you are losing it, try scented powders in spots where you have a tendency to perspire. How about under your breast, on the inside of your thighs, inside you elbows and even on your feet or in your shoes, before you slip into them. You can use powders under your arms — after you've applied your deodorant.

- **NO MERMAID, I:** To get rid of the dry skin scales from your legs, buttocks, and anywhere else, tie a mixture of equal parts of Epsom salts and ordinary table salt into a piece of muslin, using a ribbon, a piece of string or a rubber band. Wet it and once you're in the bath or shower, massage your entire body (except breasts and genitals), giving extra attention to problem spots, such as heels and elbows. Rinse with lukewarm-water, drip dry and apply my *Skin Correction Body Treatment Creme*.

• **HOW-DOES-MY-GARDEN-GROW BATH OIL:** If it has petals and grows in your garden, you can use it to make a delightful bath oil. Collect petals from your favorite garden flowers, put them in a wide-mouthed glass container and cover them with warmed salad oil. Keep the jar in the sun or some other warm place for a week to ten days until the fragrance of the petals permeates the oil. Strain out the petals. Check the aroma of the oil. Of course, the more aromatic the flowers you select, the more fragrant your personalized Garden Bath Oil will be. If needed, add a few drops of your favorite essential oil—something like Lavender, Geranium, Neroli (orange blossom), Rose or Jasmine. Decant into a dark-colored bottle with a stopper and keep it in the fridge until you're ready to pour a small quantity into your bath water. These scented oils also make a great personalized gift for lovers of organic and natural products.

• **BABY YOURSELF:** If you have some baby oil left at home but all of your babies are gone—try this. Using your favorite essential oils, anything from Bergamot to Ylang-Ylang, add a few drops at a time to the baby oil. When the fragrance reaches a level that pleases you, pour the mixture into a dark-color glass container with a cover. Store in the fridge until you need a special pick-me-up in your bath water. A Tablespoon or two will scent a whole tub full of water with a light fragrance that won't conflict with your perfume.

• **WAR OF THE ROSES:** If you've had problems with your bath products fighting your cologne or perfume, here's a solution. To four Tablespoons of olive or baby oil, add one teaspoon of your favorite scent. Swirl into your bathwater. Although I think my *Hand and Body Lotion* has a delightful aroma, if you want all of your fragrances to match, add about 6 drops of your favorite perfume (not cologne) to my Lotion. Check the scent; if you can still detect the light fragrance in my lotion, add more of your perfume, drop by drop.

- **FEETS, DON'T FAIL ME NOW:** When your feet perspire and get hot and tired, they can make all of you hot and tired. Believe me I know. I've spent many a day standing in department and specialty stores doing Show & Tell demonstrations for hundreds of women. My tricks for feeling better instantly:

  - I take off my shoes and air them out for a few minutes. Then I dust scented talcum powder right into the shoes.

  - My favorite foot-cooler of all—I spray my favorite cologne right onto my feet. It can't be beat for foot relief.

  - If my feet are hot and sweaty before I even start my day, I also spray my cologne onto the feet of my panty hose, letting it dry for a few minutes before I slip into them. Wonderful cooler.

- **LEG TREATMENT:** You should moisturize your legs even more frequently than you do the rest of your body. Why? Because there are very few working oil glands in the skin on your legs. That's why your legs have a tendency to be drier than other spots. You should also consider using oil on your legs as a substitute for shaving cream. Remember—bubbles tend to be drying and shaving creams are full of tiny bubbles. With oil as the lubricant when you shave your legs, they will end up being silky smooth.

- **DO-IT-YOURSELF BATH MITT:** Very simple and easy to make. Sew together two washcloths—completely on three sides and on the fourth, leave a center opening large enough for your bar of soap to slip through. Put the soap inside and massage your skin, all over.

- **SOAP VERSUS BATH GELS:** Which you use is really a matter of personal choice. Both soap and gels cleanse; both are available in a variety of scents; both come in a wide price range; and both have selections which lather lots or lather little. The one area where there is a difference—with gels you won't get a "ring around the bathtub" because the gels do not react with hard water' as soap does.

IDEAS ABOUT SUPERFLUOUS HAIR

Now that your body is bathed, perfumed, moisturized, exfoliated, brushed, loofahed and oiled, it's time to examine the issue of superfluous or unwanted hair. Getting there is not half the fun when you're seeking a sleek, hairless body. But, the alternative is not attractive to look at. So let me share the best ways I've learned and heard about on the subject.

ALL ABOUT WAXING: As far as temporary hair removal is concerned, waxing is the longest-lasting method—three to six weeks, depending on the area of the body and also on the individual growth rate of your hair. I prefer however, to leave my waxing to the professionals in the beauty salons.

At home you can wax with either a cold wax or a hot wax. Both kinds are sold at the local drugstore. Hot wax is sold in a bar form; cold wax is sold attached onto tape or sheets of paper. Cold wax is simpler to do; but, hot wax does a better job and lasts longer.

To remove hair with cold wax, you press the paper, waxy side facing the surface to be waxed and then pull up the sheets, hopefully with the superfluous hair attached. Read the instructions on the packaging before you start. When you use hot wax, you must heat it until it melts. Be sure to test a drop or two on an area of skin which is not to tender, before you apply it all over, to make sure it's not too hot. Again, read the instructions before you start. Apply the heated wax with a large brush, stroking in the direction the hair grows. Pull it off in the opposite direction. Do not brush the hot wax on warts or moles, or on irritated, burned, broken out, cut skin or skin with a rash. Again, test first—both for heat and for your skin's reaction. By the way, if you're rating this procedure for comfort—on a scale of one to ten—ten being extremely uncomfortable, waxing earns a rating of 11.

Some tips on the whole waxing scene are listed below. But first, if it's at all possible, have yourself waxed at least once at a good beauty salon so you can see how the licensed aestheticians do it. Okay. Now you're ready—hopefully. Read through these instructions first, before you start your waxing session.

1. Cleanse the area to be waxed thoroughly, with witch hazel applied to a cotton ball.

2. After drying off your skin, dust it with talcum powder. Lightly, please.

3. Legs & Arms—your re-growth should be about 1/4 inch. Face—remove any traces of creams or makeup.

4. Position the waxing cloth on the area to be waxed.

5. Brush on the heated wax, in the same direction in which the hairs grow.

6. Let the wax harden.

7. Pull the skin taut with your left hand (right, if you're a south-paw) and, with your right hand, give a hard tug and lift off the cloth and wax in one swift motion for the least ouch and the best results. It's a case 'bite the bullet' and get it over with.

8. Apply finger pressure to newly waxed areas to prevent the formation of water blisters.

LEG WAXING TRICKS: Start with the calves of the legs. Because the calves are less sensitive than other areas, you'll have a chance to perfect your skills before you get to the more delicate areas. To present a smooth surface for applying the wax, bend your knee. Continue on to the outer thighs and then the inner thighs. In both cases, hold your skin taut while brushing on the wax. Whatever hairs you do not get this time, you'll have to leave until a later time. You're skin will be irritated from the first go-around, so a second application and removal would hurt too much.

To determine where to place the wax for a bikini line removal, don a pair of high-cut bikini underpants. The edge of the panties will act as a guide for the bathing suit line. With a small pair of sharp scissors, trim off all of the hairs that show below the line to about one-fourth of an inch. Tuck a folded paper towel inside your panties to keep from dripping wax onto the pubic hair you do not want to wax. Sit on an old towel on the bathroom floor. (I forgot to tell you, you have to be contortionist in order to do this. But, I guess if you're wearing a bikini, we don't have to worry about your agility.) Wax and pull from the outer edge, inwards. When you get to the area above the crotch, spread your legs outward and work in small sections. Doing your own bikini waxing is such an awkward process that you may decide it's worth the $15 to $35 cost of a professional beauty salon waxing.

WHEN?: Since there is redness and irritation, wax a few days before you leave on vacation. If you're going away for more than three weeks, bring along your waxing kit. (Or, pamper yourself with a bikini waxing at the resort's beauty salon. After all, you are on vacation. Be sure to make your appointment well in advance because many women schedule their bikini waxing at these locations. Regrowth in the bikini area is faster than regrowth on other sections of the body. By the fourth week, you'll need another bikini waxing.

WAXING AND THE LIPLINE: When you wax your upper lip area, you must be very careful so that no hot wax drips onto your lips—they are very delicate. Apply the wax, diagonally from just beneath one nostril to the outer corner of the mouth on the same side of the face. To remove the wax, hold-the skin just beneath the area with the wax as taut as possible. In one quick, diagonal upwards tug, pull off the wax. Repeat the process on the other side.

IMPORTANT: TO PREVENT WATER BLISTERS FROM FORMING, APPLYING FINGER PRESSURE ON THE NEWLY WAXED AREA.

WAXING ARMS/UNDERARMS: If you don't have hair on any of the following areas, start from the point where your hair growth begins. When it comes to your arms, you work from bottom to top—fingers, backs of the hands, side of the arm (from thumb to elbow), the front of the arm and lastly, the back of the arm. Follow Steps 1 through 8, as described on pages 138-139. A tip for doing the backs of the arms—place the palm of your hand (of the arm you're waxing) on the opposite shoulder and apply the wax from underneath. As far as your underarms are concerned—put the hand of the underarm to be waxed behind your head. Apply the wax in two segments: from the middle of your armpit to the top; then, from the middle of your armpit to the bottom. Pull the wax off with one "fell swoop". (I've always wanted to be able to use that expression.) If there are some stragglers you missed, I'd suggest plucking them out with a pair of tweezers unless you have an unbelievably high pain threshold. If you have a low pain threshold—do not attempt the underarms.

CHIN UP: Brush the hot wax to the area of the chin being waxed. When the wax has hardened, pull the skin on the neck, under the chin taut with your fingers. Remove the wax in one quick tug.

TUMMY HAIR?: To eliminate that line of hair that grows from the navel to the top of the pubic area, brush the wax onto your skin from the bottom to the top. Pull off the wax in one smooth swoop, from the navel down. If by any chance, your hair grows the opposite way, reverse the two procedures.

LEAVE IT TO EXPERTS: Because of the proximity to the eyes, I would leave waxing your eyebrows to professional salon personnel. It's too easy to drip hot wax in your eyes. This is truly not a do-it-yourself project. Eyebrow waxing runs in the area from $6 to $16 depending on where you live and the kind of salon you patronize.

DEODORANT WOES: What can you do if you find yourself allergic to antiperspirants or deodorants? Try talcum powder, baking soda or rubbing a bar of moist soap in the underarm area. You could also try witch hazel—but definitely not right after you've shaved under your arms. A mixture of vinegar and water will also work; by the time you leave the house, the odor of vinegar will have evaporated.

QUICK TIPS FOR SHAVING: If you shave your legs, bikini line or under your arms, you probably have more ingrown hairs than the average. Massaging with a loofah these areas lightly when you're in the bath or shower, will help these ingrown hairs to reach the surface of the skin. Incidentally it's to prevent ingrown hairs that shaving in the direction of the hairs' growth is recommended. To soften the hair and making shaving easier, drape a hot, wet towel on the area to be shaved and leave it on for five minutes. When shaving the bikini area, do it twice—once in the direction the hair grows; the second time, the opposite way. And dust the area lightly with talcum as soon as you're finished.

NICK, NICK: Should you cut yourself when you're shaving, pat a small piece of toilet paper over the nick and apply finger pressure for about two minutes. If you have the "nick habit", keep a styptic stick in your bathroom. Anytime you wax or shave, you may have itching— a sign that the minor irritation caused, is healing. There are several things you can do to relieve the itch.

1. Slice open a Vitamin E capsule and rub its contents into the affected area.

2. Cornstarch will soothe the skin if you dust it lightly over the shaved or waxed area.

3. Zephiran Chloride, an antiseptic found in the pharmacy can be used for two mornings and evenings after your wax or shave, as a preventative. Apply it to the area with a cotton ball. It tends to forestall the reddish rashes that may appear after your hair removal sessions.

CHAPTER SIX
PERSONAL FITNESS

You've probably heard me say hundreds of times that I'm a physical fitness nut when it comes to eating properly and exercising. I'm out there every day—walking, jogging or riding a bicycle—depending on whether I'm at home in the city, away for the weekend or vacation, or on the road, appearing on a television shopping program or at seminars in the major department stores around the world. And, there's never a whole day when I'm not watching every morsel I put into my mouth, to make sure that it's good for all parts of my body, as well as for my weight. That does not mean that I never pop a sinful chocolate covered cherry into my mouth. I do; but, you can bet that it won't be more than one nor will I do it every day. I know that there's a choc-o-holic hovering inside of me. That's where "she's" going to stay! By the way, over 50% of women who were recently asked what they would change about their physical appearance said "My weight". Currently in the United States, the average women's dress size is 14, she weighs 144 lbs and is almost 5'4" tall. It's also estimated that about thirty million American women regularly purchase Size 16.

Years ago, I did not have a regular exercise routine. Now, I keep an image of how I want to look in my mind's eye and work towards it every day. This chapter is written for those of you who are not yet completely convinced that you can improve your physical well-being by a combination of proper nutrition and increase physical activity. Exercise, in addition to improving your physical health has some wonderful side benefits. In addition to firming up all parts of your body, physical activity relieves stress, increases your self-esteem and in general helps you to feel great. On the physical side, regular exercise helps the body to maintain and repair itself, no matter how old you are or how inactive you've been. The heart and lungs are strengthened; body fat is reduced; your blood pressure can be lowered and your joints will stay or become more flexible.

FOR BEGINNERS: GET YOUR BODY MOVING

The most difficult part is convincing yourself to give it a try. I'll admit that there has been much confusion in recent years about how much exercise is good for you—how far, how long, how many, how often, how vigorous? There have been 10 different answers to each of those questions. For years, the main theory was that we'd improve our health and live longer if we exercised three times a week for 20 minutes or so in a stretch. An alternative was scheduling three 10-minute sessions every weekday and taking the week-end off. The next theory stated that all adults should string together about a half-hour of such things as gardening, walking, walking up some stairs, every day of the week. It was considered okay to do ten minutes, at a time. Most recently, studies have shown that vigorous exercise, such as walking at a fast pace—four or five miles per hour—riding a bicycle, doing housework (not light), swimming with gusto, are necessary in order to be fit. The one thing I am sure of: All Exercise Is Good. And, to lose one pound, you have to burn up 3,500 calories, eliminate 3500 calories from your diet or some combination of food intake and exercise that gives a net loss of 3,500 calories. My recommendation, once you've gone through the 15-question checklist below and come out with all "no" answers, get started doing something on a regular basis.

NO **YES**

Have you ever

☐ ☐ - had a cardiac condition or heart problems of any kind?

☐ ☐ - taken blood pressure medication?

☐ ☐ - had fainting spells or bouts of dizziness?

☐ ☐ - had or have chest pain or pressure as a result of exertion?

☐ ☐ - had periods of uneven/irregular heart beats?

☐ ☐ - been diagnosed as having high cholesterol, lipids or triglycerides?

☐ ☐ - smoked or now smoke over a pack of cigarettes a day?

☐ ☐ - had (or have) a relative such as a parent, child, sister or brother who had a heart attack prior to age 50?

☐ ☐ Are you overweight by more than 50 lbs.?

☐ ☐ Do you have shortness of breath after climbing stairs?

☐ ☐ Do you take birth control pills and smoke more than 10 cigarettes a day?

☐ ☐ Do you have a bad back, muscular problems, serious varicose vein problems and/or joint or muscular problems?

☐ ☐ Are you pregnant?

☐ ☐ Are you over 60 and consider yourself to be sedentary?

☐ ☐ Can you think of any other reason why you shouldn't start a physical fitness program?

If you answer "yes" to any of these questions, before you begin any exercise program, consult with, and follow the advice of your doctor. On the other hand, if you answer "no" to all fifteen questions, it's likely that you'll have no problems with the activities described herein. Of course, it never hurts to check in with your doctor before starting anything that affects your well-being.

If you haven't been exercising at all, Think Small. Begin by telling your mate that you'll walk the dog every morning (or evening), starting today. Or, when you're out shopping, don't look for a spot right opposite the entrance; park further and further away, each time you go—until you're walking at least a half-mile to get to your destination. Take a walk with a friend every day, leisurely to start; briskly when you've been at it for one or two weeks. I'm sure you get the idea. The main thing is to do things that fit into your life-style, so that you will do them on a regular basis.

"E" IS FOR EFFORT: Some of the exercises I'm writing about in this chapter sound relatively easy. They are; but don't fool yourself. You have to do even the easy-sounding activities with energy. You must exert yourself and truly make real effort. If you lift your arms in the air half-heartedly or barely lift your leg off the floor when the exercise calls for a leg lift, you're just fooling yourself. Your body won't be fooled; it's won't get trimmer, slimmer or more toned. I know. I've been there. There was a time when I wasn't a willing participant in my exercise routine. I had to talk myself into starting, every day, for the longest time. One trick I discovered was getting a three-pound set of dumbbells and a two pound set of ankle weights. That way, even if I was less than enthusiastic when I "faked" my way through my exercises, I got some benefit from my work-out.

ONE, TWO, THREE: There are actually three types of exercises you should use if your intention is to lose weight as well as become fit—in the beginning, at least one of each type, each day you exercise. These are:

ONE: FLEXERS are activities such as stretching, which are geared to bring flexibility to your joints and muscles. (See page 151-152 for leg, upper body and abdominal activities which increase your flexibility. Start with one flexing stretch in conjunction with one calorie-using activity in the beginning.

TWO: CALORIE USERS are exercises designed to use up calories as well as improve your overall health. These exercises involve the large muscles of the body, such as those in your legs. These activities are also are moderately intense rhythmic and repetitive in nature. When you first start, schedule one of these exercises a day, five or six days a week and work your way up to three a day. Your heart beat and your rate of breathing should be slightly elevated when involved with Calorie Users; you should be perspiring lightly and you should feel a pull in the muscles you're using. When you start out, your pace should be slower for about two minutes; then increase your pace gradually, to a moderate one. The last two minutes of your exercise session should again be at a slower pace. Examples of Calorie Users are:

- riding a bicycle
- walking
- gardening
- climbing stairs
- using home fitness equipment such as a treadmill, bicycle, rower, climber, etc.
- swimming
- jumping rope
- square dancing, line dancing, etc., etc., etc.

REGARDLESS OF WHICH OF THESE YOU SELECT, IF YOU EXPERIENCE ANY PRESSURE OR PAIN IN YOUR CHEST OR ARMS, ANY DIZZINESS, AN IRREGULAR HEART BEAT, SEVERE SHORTNESS OF BREATH OR NAUSEA—*STOP EXERCISING AND GET IN TOUCH WITH YOUR PHYSICIAN.*

THREE: MUSCLE TONERS do just that—firm and tone your muscles. In the beginning, include one Muscle Toner in your regimen along with your Calorie Burner and Flexer. You should alternate the group of muscles you tone from day to day. In other words, if you tone your upper body muscles the first day, work on your legs the next day and on your abdominal muscles on the third day. However, both your Flexer and your Muscle Toner should be from the same group of muscles on a daily basis. After you've been involved with your exercise regimen for a few weeks, you should be able to complete about 20 repetitions a day—i.e., 20 push ups, 20 arm curls or 20 head and shoulder lifts. It should take about nine seconds to complete one repetition—three seconds to move, a three-second hold and three seconds to return to the start-up position. Your movements should be controlled and slow, while breathing normally.

SPOT EXERCISE: You may have heard that it's possible to do certain exercise to reduce certain spots on your body. Not so! There is no relationship between muscles and fat. An exercise involving leg lifts, for example, may tone the muscles on your legs; but, you will not lose an ounce of fat from your legs as a result.

♦ **INNER-THIGH TONER:** Here's an inner-thigh toner you can

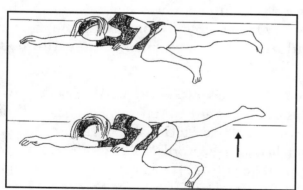

start today. All you need is the floor and a pillow. Lie down on your side with the bottom arm stretched out above your head. Place the pillow next to your body, from the shoulders to the buttocks. Rest your other arm on the pil-low. Place the top knee on the pillow, about waist high, resting your foot on the floor. Keeping your bottom knee straight, lift your leg as high as you can, holding it up for a count of three before returning it to the starting position. Do this five times and reverse positions, for five movements with the other leg. Increase the number of inner-thigh slimmers you do by three each day, until you reach fifty with each leg. Continue these slimmers until your inner thighs look the way you want them to. Then follow this routine three times a week, to keep them that way.

* **ABDOMINAL TONER:** Lie down on the floor, with your knees bent and your heels as close to your buttocks as possible. Cross your arms behind your head, with the right hand near your

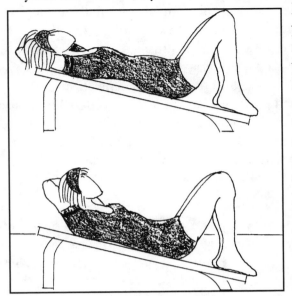

left shoulder and your left hand at your right shoulder. Lift your shoulders and head towards your chest, slowly without using your hands and arms to help. When you've lifted as high as you can, hold the position for a count of three. Do not lift your back from the floor. Return to your original position for a count of three. Start by doing four or six sets a day and work your way up to 20 per day, four days a week. Fitness gurus believe that the best abdominal muscle workout program combines an exercise such as this one with exercises which involve the entire body, including the "abs".

WALKING, WALKING WALKING: Brisk walking can help you to get to a state of physical fitness and to stay there. What is a brisk walk? Start walking and singing "Old McDonald Had a Farm". When you have to take a breath between the words "Old" and "Farm" you've just started to walk faster than "brisk". If you pump your arms when you walk, you'll increase the number of calories you burn. By the way, if you walk three miles per minute, or it takes you 20 minutes to walk a mile, you can burn up to 4 calories per minute. That means a 20-minute mile, could use up 80 calories. If you walk a mile in 12 minutes, you can use up to ten calories a minute or 360 calories in half an hour of walking. Walking is probably the easiest aerobic exercise you can attempt. Basically all you need is a good pair of walking shoes and some comfortable clothes. In the beginning, you'll also want a flat terrain; as you get more into walking, you can attempt hills—but do it gradually or your calf muscles will shriek. Walking uses all of the large muscle groups in the legs including the quadriceps and the hamstrings. The shoulder muscles will also be toned if you pump your arms as you walk. If you can't find a friend with whom to walk, get yourself a small portable cassette player with earphones. Be sure you play music with an upbeat tempo or your walking may turn into a stately procession, which defeats your purpose. By the way you should never wear earphones if you are walking where there is traffic. Scenic areas are generally more interesting and safer, so you might want to drive to a nearby waterfront or park. At the very least, vary your itinerary frequently.

STICK-TO-IT: Once you've gotten started, the trick is to stick to it. Don't set yourself up for failure by setting unrealistic goals, such as promising to walk two miles a day right from the start. Start slowly and one day at a time, increase the distance you walk, the length of time, the frequency or the energy you expend as you perform your chosen exercise. For example, if your selected activity is riding a bicycle—the first day you could just ride around the block, slowly. Try to do that twice more, the first week. By the end of the fourth week, you could be riding up to a mile a day, five days a week. Next, you might consider increasing the speed with which you ride. Then start including an uphill stretch on your daily itinerary. By the end of a month, you could be cycling 5 miles a day, through hill and dale.

GROUP THERAPY: One way to make sure you stick to your routine is to exercise with a friend or with a group. Making it into a semi-social activity, seems to increase commitment and help people maintain their activity program.

1 FROM COLUMN "A" & 1 FROM COLUMN "B": Some exercise experts suggest that for general physical fitness, you walk three to five times a week, for a minimum of thirty minutes. To *improve* your fitness quotient *and* achieve weight loss, they recommend combining 20 to 60 minutes of an aerobic exercise, such as walking, cycling or swimming, three to five times a week, with a twice a week "weight lift set", repeated eight, ten or twelve times. Your weight lifts can involve lifting your own weight via push ups or lunges, lifting weights on machines or lifting free weights, such as dumb bells. Check out my dumb-bell workout, below. If you want to become involved in a real serious weight training program, I suggest you get some expert advice. To get the names of personal trainers, you can phone the American Council on Exercise Hotline—1-(800) 825-3636. Another alternative is to join a gym which features weight training.

DUMB-BELLS FOR NEW-BELLES AKA BEGINNERS:

Don't start full speed ahead on this or any other exercise program. Before you lift any weights, do some simple warm up stretches such as leg shakes, arm swings, skipping in position and/or waist bends. (These are just what they sound like.) A few minutes worth will be fine. Do the same stretches when you finish with the weights. Incidentally, none of following should be done if you have back problems unless you've cleared them with your doctor. Here are a few firm exercises with weights which virtually any beginner can do.

◆   **BUST-FIRMER:** With a two or three pound weight in each hand, lie on the floor, knees bent with your lower back firmly pressed

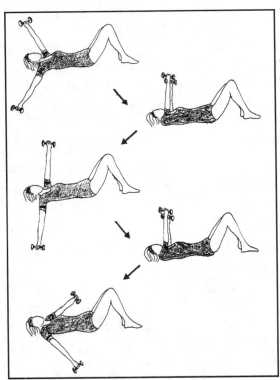

downwards and your arms outstretched flat on the floor, level with your shoulders. Raise your arms above your shoulders, bring your hands together and hold for a count of three. Return to the original position. Repeat 10 to 15 times. Next move your arms, still on the floor, until they're 45 degrees below your bosom. Raise your arms above your shoulders, bring your hands together and hold for a count of three. Return to the original position. Repeat 10 to 15 times. Now, slide your arms to a position 45 degrees above the shoulders, arms still on the floor. Raise your arms above your shoul-ders, bring your hands together and hold for a count of three. Return to the original position. Repeat 10 to 15 times.

◆ **WAIST-TRIMMER:** With two or three pound weights, one in each hand, stand on a level surface with your feet 12 inches apart. With your knees bent slightly, bend sideways from the waist and slowly slide one hand along the side of the body towards the knees, lifting the other hand and curving it above your head. Without lifting your feet, gently bounce three to five times. Reverse positions and repeat these motions. Perform ten repetitions of the set, making sure you keep your body straight and your knees bent. You'll find that you'll be able to slide a little lower each time.

◆ **TUMMY-FLATTENER:** Stand on a level surface,

with feet about 18 to 24 inches apart so that you're still balanced as you move around. With two to three pound weights, one in each hand, bring your arms out to your sides and upwards until they're at a level with your shoulders. Keeping your body straight, twist your body slowly, as far to the right as you can. Your arms will swing with the motion, one to the front; one to the back. Return to the original position and in one continuous motion, reverse the activity, swinging to your left. Continuing these slow rhythmic motions, for a total of 10 to 15 repetitions of the complete set.

BEFORE & AFTER: If you've watched me on television, you know I'm famous for my Before & After pictures. This is different. Your exercise regimen should also include warm-ups and cool-downs. Flexers, also known as Stretches, which increase your flexibility, are probably the simplest before and after exercise activities you can do. Pre-exercise stretches reduce the possibility of pulling a muscle or a tendon. Plan on doing at least three to five stretches before your daily exercise, holding the stretch for 30 seconds, as well as three to five stretches afterwards. The stretches after your aerobic exercise, which help prevent soreness the next day, should be from a different muscle group than from those you do before. That means if you do an Upper Body Stretch before walking, chose a Leg Stretch afterwards and so on. Muscle Toner exercises should also be followed with a Stretch—but in this case, from the same muscle group.

EXAMPLES OF FLEXERS

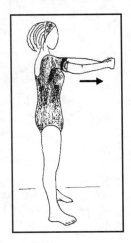 

UPPER BODY FLEXER A: Turn your palms away from you and intertwine your fingers. With a pressing motion, stretch your arms away from your body. (Hold for 30 seconds)

UPPER BODY FLEXER B: With a towel in hand, put your one hand on your back, in between your shoulder blades. With the other hand, grab the end of the towel from below. Move the fingers of each hand towards each other. Reverse the hands and repeat.

UPPER BODY FLEXER C: Intertwine your fingers behind your buttocks. Lift the hands away from your backside. (Hold for 30 seconds.)

UPPER BODY FLEXER D: Drop your shoulders. Stretch one arm across your body and, with the other hand, gently push the elbow of the outstretched arm further across the front of you. Reverse positions and repeat. (Hold each stretch for 30 seconds)

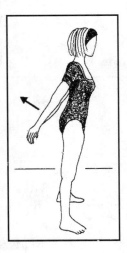 

ABDOMINAL FLEXER A: With the knees bent and the toes pointing forwards, grab the knees with the hands and tilt the buttocks back to form the letter "C" with your body. By the way the abdominal muscles are also called the "ABs", colloquially. (Hold for 30 seconds)

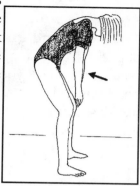

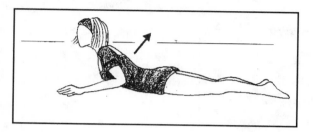

ABDOMINAL FLEXER B: Lie face down on the floor, with you palms down, underneath your shoulders. Pressing down on your hands, lift your head up and away from the floor while arching your back. Tighten the buttocks. (Hold for 30 seconds)

LEG FLEXER A: With one leg extended, put your foot on a chair.

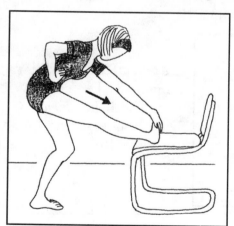

Bend the other leg. Keeping your back flattened, grab the toes on the chair with your opposite hand. Reverse legs and repeat. (Hold each stretch for 30 seconds)

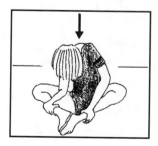

LEG FLEXER B: Sit on the floor and put both feet together, soles facing each other. Holding your ankles, lean forward until your head almost touches your legs. (Hold for 30 seconds)

LEG FLEXER C: Place one palm against the wall. With the other hand, reach back and grab the toes on the opposite foot. Using a light pressure, pull your heel towards your buttocks. Reverse positions and repeat. (Hold each stretch for 30 seconds)

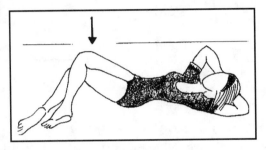

LEG FLEXER D: Placing your hands under your head, lie down on the floor, on your back. Bend your knees and cross one knee over the other allowing the knees to drop onto the side of the knee that's on the top. Reverse position and repeat. (Hold each stretch for 30 seconds)

EXAMPLES OF MUSCLE TONERS

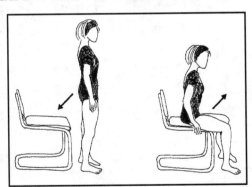

LEG TONER A: Sit in a straight-backed chair. With your head held high and your back straight, stand up and sit down. Repeat from 1-20 times.

LEG TONER B: Lie down on the floor, on your side. Bend your knees. Lift the upper leg away from the lower leg, keeping both knees bent. Return the upper leg to the original position. Roll onto the other side and repeat with the other leg. Repeat this combo from 1-20 times.

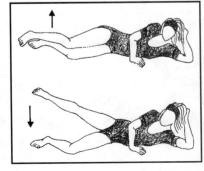

LEG TONER C: Stand an arm's length away from the wall, feet flat on the floor, toes pointed towards the wall. Stretch out your arms and press your palms, lightly, against the wall. Rise up onto your toes and return to the original position. Repeat 1-20 times.

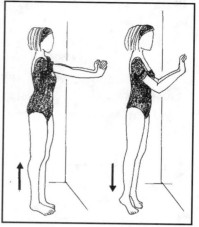

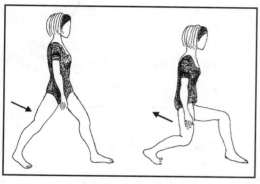

LEG TONER D: Stand up straight, one leg thrust forward. Kneel with one leg. Stand up. Reverse legs and kneel with the other leg. Repeat 1-20 times.

UPPER BODY TONER A: Stand erect, with your feet apart, your arms at your sides, with your palms turned forwards. Curl your hands, bend your arms, bringing your hands up to your shoulders. Return to the original position. Repeat 1-20 times.

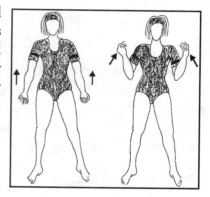

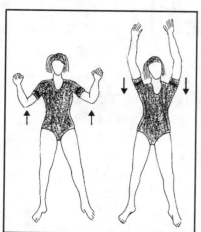

UPPER BODY TONER B: Stand erect, with feet apart, your arms at your sides, hands curled. Keeping your arms at the side, reach over your head as far as you can. Return your arms to the original position. Repeat 1-20 times.

UPPER BODY TONER C: Stand about three feet away from the wall, facing it. Place both palms flat on the wall, in front of your shoulders. Bending your arms, lean forward towards the wall and push back again. Repeat 1-20 times.

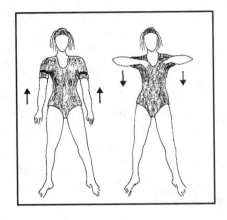

UPPER BODY TONER D: Stand erect, with feet apart, arms hanging at your sides, palms facing inwards. Raise your elbows out to the sides and bring your hands to your under-arms. Return your arms to the original position. Repeat 1-20 times.

ABDOMINAL TONER A: Lie on the floor, on your back. Bring your knees above your pelvic cavity, with your ankles crossed. Move your knees above your chest. Return to the original position. Cross your ankles the other way and repeat. Repeat the combination 1-20 times.

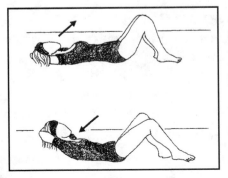

ABDOMINAL TONER B: Lie on the floor, on your back with your knees bent, your hands clasped behind your head and your chin tilted downwards. Lift your head and shoulders as far as you can. Return to the original position. Repeat 1-20 times.

WHAT IS "AEROBIC" ANYWAY? When it comes to your body, aerobic involves exercises that condition the heart and lungs, which consequently increase the body's efficiency of taking in oxygen. If you get breathless while walking or cycling, your exercise is no longer aerobic: it is then anaerobic. Another benefit of aerobic exercise is that 15 or 20 minutes of aerobics will keep your mood on the positive side for several hours after you stop exercising.

SKIP-TO-MY-LOU: One of my all-time favorite exercises is skipping rope, primarily because you can do it just about any place and there's virtually no cost or equipment involved. It's especially good on rainy days when I can't jog and on occasions when I'm traveling and don't have the time to jog in the daylight. It's good for your legs and the entire cardiovascular system. Skipping rope is serious exercise; don't think you start off by doing 500 jumps in a row the first day. You can't and even if you could, you shouldn't. If you are really out of shape, start with as few as five a day. If you're in fairly decent shape but just haven't been particularly active, start with a maximum of 25 a day. Either way, gradually work your way up to five hundred a day, five days a week. Once you're really into it, it shouldn't take you more than five or ten minutes a day. And remember to warm up and cool down with the simple stretches I described earlier.

A WAKE-UP STRETCHER: "Start exercising while I'm still in bed? Are you dreaming?" It's just a gentle activity you can do every morning while you're still in bed. You can even keep your eyes closed through the entire stretch. You'll feel very virtuous when you've done it. Sit up with your legs extended and your toes pointed. Take ten deep breaths. Intertwine your fingers and raise your arms above your head for a count of ten. Lower your arms towards your toes. Hold for a count of ten. Return your arms towards their original position, unclasp your hands, relax your shoulders and drop your hands to your sides. Rotate your head slowly, starting from a chin-down position. Hold for a count of five at each—the left shoulder, the middle of the back, the right shoulder, ending where you started. That's it. It takes longer to write about it than to do it.

EAT, EAT: That's right. Eating is good for you. You should not go without eating for hours and then exercise. Your body needs an on-going supply of carbohydrates, which become blood sugar, to keep it moving. That means, if you exercise in the morning, have some carbohydrates about an hour before you start—a toasted English muffin or a bagel. If you exercise late in the day, eat small amounts of low-in-fat, high-in-carbohydrates during the day. If you are on an eating regimen, don't add these carbohydrates to your in-take. Make them part of your daily food allocation. Conversely, don't cram a huge meal or a sack of chips into your mouth just before you start your exercises or you'll have a tendency to experience stomach cramps.

WATER: You already know that it's important to drink six to eight glasses of water a day. However, if you're on an exercise program, it's important that you drink eight ounces of water about 15 minutes before you start. The body needs the water to cool itself down and keep you on the move for the duration of your daily exercises. Once you get to where your physical activity exceeds twenty minutes at a stretch, keep sipping water throughout your workout. Incidentally, instead of carrying one large water bottle while you're walking, jogging or running, carry two or three smaller ones. Distribute them around your body so they'll be much easier to carry. Also if one develops a leak, you will still have a reserve.

MUSCLES INSTEAD OF FLAB: I'm not talking about muscles like Mr. America or the tanned specimens who strut around the local Muscle Beach. Women are lucky—because they are not over-endowed with the male testosterone hormone, exercise will not bulk up female muscles as a result of exercise. Rather, physical activity will firm up the flesh and—hooray, hooray—muscle takes less space than fat does. That's what's meant when people say they haven't lost weight but that they have lost inches. It doesn't make any difference to me what I weigh, as long as I look as trim as I want to and fit easily into the clothes in my wardrobe.

RELAXERCISE #1: Not all exercises are designed to firm, tone and trim. Some are meant to help you relax and un-stress. Breathing deeply is one of the best Relaxercises known to the human race. Whenever you get stressed out, when you feel like you can't go on at the same hectic pace, or even when you're tempted to reach for a piece of candy or a handful of pretzels—take a deep breath. The nice thing is you can do it anywhere—in meetings, while dining in a gourmet restaurant, at a movie or listening to a boring conversation hog at a party. Taking a full, deep breath relaxes the same part of the nervous system that produces the flow of adrenaline when you're anxious, aggravated or otherwise stressed. Really up-tight? Add a two or three second "Hold" when you're at the fullest point of the inhaling portion of your deep breath. Then exhale very deeply and do another three second "Hold". Those "Holds" will trigger your heart to slow-up it's pace a bit for a few moments—enough so an unwinding process gets started. To finish up, sit up straight in a comfortable chair. Close your eyes. For about two minutes, take deep breaths with your hand resting on the top of your head. Each time you exhale, imagine your breath leaving your body through your hand. Doesn't that feel great?

RELAXERCISE #2: Neck and shoulders achy from spending too much time hunched over your computer? They even got a name for this problem—Upper Cross Syndrome; it's traits are: a head that tilts forward, neck and back muscles which are weakened and tightened chest muscles. Use the following Relaxerciser when you feel the UCS tightening coming on:

Stand up straight, with your arms extended above your head, about 36" apart, elbows slightly bent, with one end of a bath towel in each hand. Tighten your abdominal muscles and slowly lower your arms to shoulder height, keeping them stretched and the towel taut. Scrunch your shoulder blades together. You'll feel a stretching sensation in your chest. Hold for a count of three and bring your arms back to the original position. Repeat this set of movements three to five times.

RELAXERCISES FOR TRAVELERS: As with other exercises, warm-ups and cool-downs are suggested. So before your get on the conveyance of choice and as soon as you get off, take a quick walk around the block, up and down the "aisles" which lead to the gates at the airport around the bus or train terminal. Once you're on board, try to follow the suggestions listed below once an hour. They will make sure you arrive at your destination feeling relatively fresh.

+ **THE AISLE WALK:** When traveling by plane, train or bus, take a trip up and down the aisle as often as possible. At the end of each stroll, bend back your knees, one at a time. Grab your foot behind your body and pull it towards your buttocks. Hold for a count of three. Repeat with the other foot.

- **THE LEG PINCH:** If you find that your legs are cramping up, starting at the top of your thighs, pinch your way down your leg towards your knees. Massage your knees for a count of three and continue down your shin bones, massaging your inner ankles to a count of three and pinch down to your toes. Come back up, massaging your outer ankles to a count of three, ending at the top of the thighs. If you can't pinch both legs simultaneously, do one at a time.

- **THE BODY STRETCHER:** Sit straight up in your seat, stretch your legs in front of you and take a deep breath. Hold for a count of three. Raise your arms slowly above your head, reaching "for the stars". Tilt your hands backwards and hold for a count of three. Lower your arms. Repeat the entire sequence three to five times. Don't forget the deep breath between each set.

HOW TO DO THE LUNGE: You've probably heard about "The Lunge" as an excellent way of toning your buttocks and thighs, as well as improving your basic agility. There are three basic types of Lunge—a Forward Lunge, a Platform Lunge and a Backwards Lunge. All three will work. I suggest you try each one to find out which one is most comfortable for you.

- **FORWARD LUNGE:** Stand on a level surface, with your feet about 18" apart. With your left leg, take one giant heel-to-toe step forward, keep your back perfectly straight. Bend your left leg so that the knee is above the ankle and it forms a 90 degree angle. Hold for a count of three and return to the original position. Reverse legs and repeat. Start with three to five lunges per day and work your way up to 15 to 20 sets.

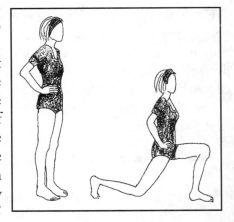

- **BACKWARDS LUNGE:** Stand on a level surface with your feet about 18" apart. Lift your leg, knee bent, so that your knee is level with your hips. Then move the lifted leg backwards, the equivalent of two steps. Hold for a count of three and return to the original position, pressing down on your  forward heel. Switch to the other leg and repeat. Start with three to five sets a day and work your way up to 15 to 20 sets.

- **PLATFORM LUNGE:** Stand about 30" behind a platform which is eight inches high. Place one foot on the platform heel-to-toe. Bend your leg to a 90 degree angle, with your knee over your ankle, keeping your back erect as you lower your body. Hold for a count of three and return to the original position, pressing your heel into the platform as you remove your foot. Switch to the other leg and repeat. Start with three to five sets per  day and gradually work up to 15 to 20 sets per day. This Lunge is particularly effective for contouring the backs of your thighs and your buttocks.

IS IT RIGHT YET: You've been exercising for several weeks now and want to know if you're exercising vigorously enough for it to classify as a good aerobic workout. You could start taking your pulse while you're walking, swimming skipping rope or jogging to find out if you're hitting that higher heartbeat that's recommended you reach for 20 minutes a day at least three times a week. Another way of finding out if your activities are on target is to ask yourself "How do I feel?" If you think that you're really not being active enough, you're probably not. If you're utterly exhausted after 20 minutes, you're working too hard and will probably end up quitting. These are the signs that will tell you that you're doing it right:

- You're perspiring; but you're not sopping wet.

- Your body is tingling; but you're not aching while you're exercising (except for the second or third day after you start an exercise program or the day after you added some uphill or other strenuous efforts to your regimen).

- You are breathing rapidly; but you're not panting so hard that you can't say "Old MacDonald Had A Farm" without taking a breath in the middle.

If you do want to check your "guess-timate" about your rate of activity against the pulse that's right for a 20 minute stretch, for someone who is starting an exercise program, here is the way to arrive at your safe, yet effective rate. Subtract your age from 220 and multiply the result, first by 50% and then by 70%. Your heartbeat should fall into the range of those two numbers. Examples for several ages:

220 - 40 year old		220 - 60 years old		220 - 50 years old	
180 x.50	180 x.70	160 x.50	160 x.70	170 x.50	170 x.70
90 to 126 pulse rate		85 to 119 pulse rate		80 to 112 pulse rate	

QUICK TIP # 1: You don't have to exercise at the same time every day. And if you skip a day once in a while, the world won't come to an end as a result. Don't get so pressured into exercising that you take the fun out of it. Stay loose.

QUICK TIP # 2: Please don't expect exercising to turn your body into that of Jane Fonda. Improve what you have to the best of your ability and your general age and health. Be realistic.

QUICK TIP #3: No matter how enthusiastic you are, if you haven't exercised in years, start slowly and with small units of exercise. Yes, there will be a little soreness and achy-ness, for a few days after you start—especially the second and third days. But if you experience real pain and/or can barely move, you've either done your exercise incorrectly or you've started too much, too soon. Don't give up though. Just back off and try again, more slowly and with smaller increments of activity.

QUICK TIP # 4: Just as your car's engine needs oil to keep it lubricated and moving properly, you need water. Water before you exercise. Water while you exercise. Water after you exercise. And, six to eight glasses of water any day you don't exercise.

QUICK TIP # 5: If there's a day when you had planned to exercise and you just don't feel up to completing the activity program you had planned, try to do a few exercises or stretches. Remember, something is better than nothing. And who knows, after you've started you might feel like doing more. Physical activity makes you feel more energetic.

CHAPTER SEVEN
CLOTHES COVERUP

One of the nicest things about being a woman is the wonderful clothes we get to wear; clothes that allow us to present ourselves at our very best. Of course in order to do that you need to learn camouflaging tricks. You've seen me perform cosmetic camouflaging magic on the face on TV; but you need to learn how to hide body flaws, too. I have given hundreds of "Dress to Camouflage your Body" Seminars in the finest department stores all over the United States and Canada. All you have to do to learn all of my tips is to read on.

One thing I want to tell you right now before I forget it. If you are on a weight-reduction program—the minute you lose 10 pounds, the equivalent of a dress size—either take in your clothes or give them away and get yourself a limited wardrobe in your new size. Not only will lack of clothing in your old size deter you from slip-sliding back up the scale; but, the slimmer you in garments that fit properly, will motivate you to stick to your program.

Now, let's take it from the top. There are some elementary things you should know. If you ever studied Art, you know that you can use line and color to fool the eye. And basically that's what you want to use your clothes for—to fool your eyes—or rather other people's eyes, so that your body flaws are not noticed.

- To make something look wider, you use horizontal lines.

- To make something look longer and thinner, you would use vertical lines.

- To place focus on a particular point, you would let your lines intersect.

- Diagonal lines that come together, make things look smaller or narrower.

- Diagonal lines which move apart, are used to make things look wider or larger.

- Shapes that are longer than they are wide, give a slimmer appearance.

- Shapes which are wider than they are long, give a fuller appearance.

- Two contrasting colors call attention to the area where they meet.

- Two like or similar colors minimize the area where they meet.

You probably want to know what to do with the above information. Just take it with you when you go shopping and you'll quickly see what I mean. Let's examine some specific problems and consider the solutions.

SHORT NECK: The best necklines for a short neck are those with lines and shapes which move the eye away from the neck and leave a bare area between the neck and the bosom. The most flattering neckline is a V-neck, a low scoop neck, a sailor collar or a rolled V-collar. If you have a Polaroid camera, take a picture of yourself in a V-necked blouse and with a turtle neck. Even before the picture is fully developed, you'll see which one makes your neck look longer.

LONG, SCRAWNY NECK: Contrary to your short-necked friends, you'll want to wear necklines that are high, with a horizontal line. A jewel or crew neckline is your best cover up. And, in the cooler weather, turtle necks and cowls camouflage this flaw very well. Of course, if you have a long, swan-like neck, you don't want to camouflage it—you want to draw attention to it. Actually, there is virtually no neckline that you cannot wear.

ROUND SHOULDERS: If drooping shoulders are your problem, it's easily solved with the proper sleeve lines. Obviously padded shoulders are the quickest solution. But, what to do when (and if) padded shoulders go out of style? Gibson Girl sleeves will work, as will a Bishop's sleeve. Epaulets are a boon to the round shouldered person. And two very pretty looks which work with lighter weight fabrics are a petal-shaped or a bell-shaped sleeve.

FOOTBALL PLAYER'S SHOULDERS: On the other hand, if Mother Nature endowed you with shoulders which would make a Quarterback proud, you should look for sleeves which have diagonal to vertical lines, rather than a horizontal-lined shoulder treatment.

Dolman or kimono sleeves work well, as does a standard shirt-type sleeve. Halter tops also work well with, because the lines converge at the neck, keeping focus away from the shoulders.

UPPER ARM FLAWS: Unfortunately, once the aging process really gets going, there's not to much that can be done, except via clothes, to correct flabby or scrawny upper arms. Gone are the days when we could wear tank tops, sleeveless summer dresses and blouses. Halters are a thing of the past and tube tops are history. Even short sleeves are usually taboo. Naturally, you can wear almost any kind of long sleeve, just not anything that is too tight. My favorite is a loose, flowing sleeve with pretty buttons at the wrist—very feminine and graceful. But, who wants to wear long sleeves in the summer. What to do? A sleeve that reaches almost to the elbow works, especially the kind that's loose fitting and flutters in a light summer breeze. These can usually be found on dresses made of very sheer or very lightweight fabric. Rolling up long sleeves so they just cover the elbows, is an excellent solution. Another way to distract the eye from upper arm problems, is to put the focus on the wrists, by wearing bracelets—the more interesting, the better.

FULL-BOSOM CAMOUFLAGE: One of the major problems of an over-abundant bosom as one hits the Great Divide (40 years of age), is that the sexy look of full breasts gives way to the look of a chest. The first rule is to abandon the clingy fabrics you loved to wear. Tops that cling just remind everyone that what you used to flaunt is now two inches lower than it was. Select necklaces that end just before the curve of your bosom starts back in towards your torso. Also select the size of your chains carefully. Too small, and your bosom over-powers them; too large a piece stands out, literally, too far. Double-breasted jackets work well on women who don't have their own. If you're amply endowed, stick with the single-breasted look. You can wear sweaters; but, please make sure that they have a nice loose fit. Also, a bra with seams is a "must" for the full-bosomed woman. There is something called a "minimizer" in which the bra's construction can reduce the appearance of an ample bosom by almost an inch. These are generally available at good lingerie shops and in catalogs for larger women. Another suggestion that's more for your comfort than anything else: look for bras with wider straps so you won't have red, angry strap marks on your shoulders every night.

The right cup size can make a big (pardon the expression) difference too, as far as cleavage is concerned. If your breasts meet each other in the middle, you are probably wearing a cup that's too small. Nowadays, you can get up to a size "H" cup, if necessary. When it comes to clothes for the bedroom, to get a little extra hold or lift, select a nightgown with a soft, built-in bra, an empire line or a gown with a stretch-lace top. None of these will make your bosom look as if you were 18; but, they will disguise a midlife droop.

SMALL BOSOM CAMOUFLAGE: If gravity is causing your just-right sized bosom to do what was suggested in that Florida commercial —"Come on down"—you have lots of options available to you. You can wear lots of tops with detailing—such as shirring, pockets, ruffles, a scoop-necked peasant look. Sweaters on loose side— not baggy—work well, especially those with lots of texture: chenille, angora, double-knit. Horizontal ribbing and horizontal patterns are much better than narrow vertical ribbing or stripes. Double-breasted jackets are perfect for you. And, the lingerie department can serve you very well: seamless under-wire bras, contour bras, bras with fibre-fill or a light polyurethane foam, molded-cup bras. In the nightgown department—those with lots of lace on top, a shirred bodice or with a draw-string under the bust-line will definitely camouflage and help you feel sexy.

WAIST TRIMMERS: In this area, color can play an important role. A waist that is heavier than you want it to be, is emphasized if you wear contrasting tops and bottoms, such as navy slacks with a white shirt. If you want to wear a two piece ouffit, a much better look would be two tones of the same color. Or, if you are in love with the light top, dark bottom look—wear the top on the outside so that the delineating line is lower than your waist. That way, the strong horizontal line won't be exactly on the spot you want to camouflage. Even if you are wearing a top and bottom of the same color, your waist will look better if your top has a longer line—tunics and long sweaters or shirts hide mid-body bulges better than anything else. Things you should shun if your waist or midriff are too large are:

- no wide belts or cummerbunds

- no shiny or bejeweled belts to call attention to the waist

- no knit dresses which cling at the waist, particularly not those with elastic waists

- no wide waistbands on slacks, shorts or skirts

- no loops on your waistbands

If you wear a body slimmer, be sure to get one with a wide band around the waist, to act as a waist cincher. Just don't go to extremes as then did when wasp-waists were in. In those days, lingerie departments sold cinchers that could literally nip inches off your mid-section. Remember the laced "iron-maiden" worn by Scarlet O'Hara? Women then believed a 19" waist was worth being tortured all day and half-way into the night. No wonder they fainted so much. Thank goodness we've smartened up.

TUMMY MASKERS: I'd suggest avoiding dirndl skirts—except the modified ones, with no gathers right in the front. Stay away from dropped waist skirts and smooth-filling straight skirts. Narrow, flat pleated skirts will camouflage a less-than-tight tummy, as will knife pleats. Any skirt with stitching or tucks at the front should hide your problem. As far as slacks are concerned, your best bet are those with flatness at the front and pleats on the sides. Baggy pants with wide legs generally work, too. Slacks with fly-fronts, full all-around gathers and extremely smooth front slacks should not be included in your wardrobe. Harem pants and leotards are definitely not friendly to your figure type. Jackets and coats should range from hip-length to three-quarters—shorter or longer and your stomach will be emphasized. The dresses which are most flattering are floats, A-lines, and those having blouson or Empire waistlines, as well as tunics or long, loose sweaters. Blouses, shirts and sweaters should not be tucked into your skirts or slacks. You should also be careful in selecting the fabrics of which your garments are made—avoid any material which has a tendency to cling. Pantyhose with control-tops help to improve the lines of a protruding stomach, as do panties with some spandex or lycra in the tummy panel.

HIDING HIPS: Should your problem be hips that are great for birthing babies but hard on fashionable clothes, don't despair. There are camouflage tricks for hips, too. When it comes to blouses, there are those that place focus on the width of your hips, such as:

sweatshirts, sweaters which end at the hips, shells, belted shirts and blousons. The hippest hip-hiders are tunics—just don't belt them or you'll defeat the purpose. Your best bets in dresses, jackets and coats: the unstructured look without buttons, a princess line, capes or ponchos, and a yoked shoulder. Interesting collar treatments can draw attention away from the hips—collars as seen a Sherlock Holmes' coat or on that of the coachmen who drove the aristocrats during the 18th and early 19th Centuries. By the way, avoid large handbags that rest on your hip. They'll make you look even hippier.

BOUNTIFUL BUTTOCKS: You have a number of choices when it comes to skirts. Look for these shapes and styles when you're shopping: dirndls and modified dirndls; tiered and flounced and circular skirts. Stay away from straight, slim-lines, tapered and pleated skirts. When it comes to pants, those with side pleats or gathers work as do knickers. Avoid smooth-tipped or hip hugger treatments. Straight legged, ankle bands and waists that are slightly gathered and wide-legged pants work better than other types. You might want to consider a relatively lightweight waist-to-knee body slimmer to keep your bulges to a minimum. Incidentally, if you wear a swimsuit, opt for boxer shorts or suit with a skirt or a sarong. In general, make sure your clothes fit well in the area of your buttocks and let the waist fall where it may. And, use unstructured shirts and jackets that hang straight down from the shoulder to below the derriere. A-line skirts and dresses are a boon to the broad who's broad where broads are broad.

DISGUISING THICK ANKLES & CALVES: If over-sized ankles and calves are your problem, here are some ideas which will help you minimize them. No shorts. No pedal pushers. Culottes are okay—but you should be at least 5'5" tall. Skirts that reach to the ankles are fine. Mid-calf skirts are the worst enemy of this flaw. Mini-skirts are not as bad, because they draw the eye upwards; but there are more flattering styles available. Gored or panelled skirts, because they have an A-like line, are okay. And as far as slacks are concerned, a long straight leg or a modified bell bottom trouser looks well, especially when worn with a higher heel or even a boot. And speaking of shoes, you can minimize the look of heavy ankles and calves by wearing shoes and stockings of the same shade.

CAN I HIDE MY TOO-THIN LEGS?: Of course you can; but before you do, make sure that they really are a figure flaw and not an asset 95% of the female population would give their eye teeth for. Okay—if you're absolutely sure your legs are indeed too thin, here are some ideas for you. Stay away from dark-colored hosiery or your legs will look even thinner. Over 25, opt for a longer hem length, keeping what is fashionable in mind. The only types of skirts you should avoid are tiered/flounced skirts and circular skirts. You can wear all the other kinds. Shorts of any kind will probably make you feel self-conscious. Pants which reach your mid-calf, such as toreadors and Capri pants were made for you. Cuffed pants also look good on your legs. You should steer clear of knickers; they do nothing for you. And jodhpurs, stirrups and tapered lines would only emphasize the thinness of your legs.

You might want to consider getting a fashion adviser to help you be objective about yourself when you're shopping. Many department and specialty stores now have Personal Shoppers who will be more than happy to help you. A good friend, with an eye for fashion, could also be extremely helpful. And, you also have to be confident enough of yourself that if she says, "That skirt makes your hips look like a Hippo's," you won't throw the hanger, the garment and anything else that's handy, at her. On second thought, perhaps you should keep your friend out of your flaw-correcting fashions and keep her as a friend. Many saleswomen are excellent guides to making their customers look good. Find one who has a clientele and wants you to come back to shop with her. She knows that if you end up buying things that hang in your closet because they don't flatter you, you won't be back to her store. My favorite saleswoman will call me at the office to say, "We just received some new suits from your favorite designer. There's one that I think will look marvelous on you. Shall I hold out a Size 4 for you to try later this week?" Nine times out of ten she's chosen something that looks wonderful and is perfect for my figure and life-style. Another clothes guru could be your hair stylist. I knew a hairdresser who worked in a department store. He'd come into the salon 30 or 40 minutes before his first client was due. He'd look at the appointment book to see who was scheduled. Then he'd walk into the store looking through the racks and counters to find items that would look well on "his women". As he cut or colored his customers' hair, he'd say, "Mrs. Jones, I saw a dress in the Regency Room that would be perfect for you to wear to your daughter's engagement party." Or "Jane, there's a pants suit that's made for you in Juniors. It's a beautiful shade of blue. It has your name on it. Why don't you take a look at it. It's on the third rack from the dressing room. You can't miss it." Maybe your stylist is interested in fashion and can make suggestions to help you. However you do it, use your wardrobe to create the most flattering looks for your figure.

CHAPTER EIGHT
A BURNING ISSUE

I've said it before. Noel Coward, English playwright, actor and composer knew what he was writing about when he wrote the words to the song "Mad Dogs and Englishmen" in 1931.

"Mad dogs and Englishmen,
Go out in the midday sun.
The Japanese don't care to,
The Chinese wouldn't dare to,
The Hindus and Argentines sleep firmly from twelve to one,
But Englishmen detest a siesta.
In the Philippines, there are lovely screens
To protect you from the glare;
In the Malay states, they have hats like plates
Which the Britishers won't wear.
At twelve noon, the natives swoon,
And no further work is done;
But mad dogs and Englishmen go out in the midday sun".

Noel Coward made only one mistake. Instead of "the midday sun", he should have written "the all day sun". Of course, despite all the warnings, from health experts, beauty experts and Noel Coward, men and women, especially the under-25 crowd, still journey for miles to sit and bake in ultra-violet rays for hours, so they can darken their skins. When you tell them how bad it is for their skins they retort, "Oh but the tan looks so great." Don't they realize that at 25 minus anything, there is virtually nothing they can do that will make them look bad. Forget mentioning that in relatively few years, their skins will look like leather, all wrinkled and dried out. They think they're indestructible and will never be older. "Just you wait, little lady; just you wait!"

I don't mean that you can't play tennis, go swimming, ski or play golf. Just follow some simple rules, the first of which is to apply and keep applying a sun screen with an SPF of 15. SPF 15 gives you complete coverage. According to the FDA, a number higher than 15 doesn't give appreciably more protection than SPF 15 does.

Sunscreens are your own personal bodyguards against premature wrinkling, against sun-generated skin cancers and leathery-looking skin. So you don't have a golden tan. With my *Real Silk Kaleidoscope Bronzing Finish* you can get a healthy glow without endangering your skin. My skin hasn't seen the light of a sunny day without protection since I was 18 years of age simply because I am so fair and burn so easily. When I was young no one's mom warned them about the sun because they didn't know what we know today. When I do sit in the sun, you'll recognize me because I'm the one who is covered from head to toe with a cotton caftan, wearing a broad brimmed hat, the widest wrap-around sun glasses sold in the world, my face and any other uncovered skin part slathered with SPF 15 lotion and a huge umbrella over all of the foregoing.

By the way, going without protection in snow country can be as bad as doing so during your tropical island vacation. That's because in addition to the direct sunlight, you are also exposed to the reflected rays of the sun. And, snow can bounce off 85% of the rays. That's really Double Jeopardy! A wind burn can be just as ugly as a sunburn. And hazy days, may be lazy days to you. But to that Lucky Old Sun, hazy days are work days and he's just as busy burning skin as he is on fair-weather days. As far as I'm concerned, the only good sunshine is the one in the song "You are my sunshine my only sunshine. You make me happy, when skies are gray." I know I sound as if I believe that there is no good reason for the sun to "roam around heaven all day". That's not exactly true. I realize that sunshine makes valuable contributions to the operation of our bodies—our endocrine, circulatory, respiratory, hormonal and metabolic systems. And then, there's the Vitamin D we need for strong bones and teeth. I can't imagine that fresh fruits and vegetables would taste as good if they grew in sun-less lands.

A primary reason for any woman's youthful look is that she does not torment her epidermis, her dermis or the other layers of with the rays of the sun. Incidentally, experts agree that the sun affects all layers of the skin. The sun destroys collagen and it can attack skin's elasticity.

"Why does the skin burn?" you want to know. Ultra-Violet rays damage the UV-sensitive proteins in your skin. In turn, the small capillaries in the upper layers of your skin start to dilate. Before long, there is swelling and reddening, and you look as if you were preparing to enter a boiled lobster look-a-like contest. It is truly a burn—like the kind you'd get if you expose your skin to a flame. The sun is one of the primary causes for destroying the collagen which forms the elasticity link-ups in the dermis. With less and less collagen, the skin starts to sag, to dry out and harden. In turn, this can lead to a condition known as keratosis, a fore-runner of skin cancer. And, sun damage to the skin is progressive. The sunburn damage you acquired when you were a Junior in high school, is sitting there, waiting for you to add another layer of damage to the skin. Your skin does not return to its virgin state.

If you give these pigment producing proteins a more gradual exposure to the sun, via a protective sunscreen, they will produce more melanin, the protein that gives you the tan look. When you tan, your system actual builds up layers of cells which do give some protection against additional UV damage.

RELUCTANT TANNING TIPS: If I haven't talked you out of acquiring a tan, at least do it as safely as possible.

1. Use a sunscreen. Fair and sensitive skin gets SPF 8 or higher. Normal skin may be able to get away with an SPF 6 or 7. Darker skin should use a SPF 5. I wouldn't suggest lower than that.

2. If you haven't been out in the sun at all, especially early in the season, start with no more than 15 minutes per day, using protection is suggested. After a week, you can increase your daily dosage by about five minutes.

3. Because of their angle during the summer months, the suns rays are strongest between 10:00 am and 3:00 pm. During this time period, replenish your sunscreen more frequently than earlier or later in the day. And, be sure to re-apply protection every time you come out of the water.

4. For more sensitive parts of your skin, where there's an even a greater tendency to burn—the nose, under your eyes, on your cheekbones, on the soles of your feet, on the tops of your breasts, behind your knees and any scar tissue you may have— use the life guard's best friend: zinc oxide. It may not look sexy while you're wearing it; but, the last I heard, blistered skin isn't considered sexy either.

5. If you run out of sunscreen, either don't go out into the sunshine or wrap yourself up like Tutankamon's mummy.

6. Even if you're not at the beach or beside the pool, wear a brimmed hat if you go outdoors on a clear, sunny day.

7. If walking, jogging or running is your choice of daily exercise, please schedule your activity for late afternoon, close to sunset or in the early morning, shortly after sunrise.

8. There are now sun glasses available which block some of the UV rays, most of the UV waves and thirdly, those which block out virtually all of the UV rays. The older we get, the more protection our eyes need from the sun, not only from preventing small blood vessels from rupturing and from becoming more prone to the development of cataracts but also from the wrinkles we get from squinting when we don't have adequate eye coverage.

A, B, C: There are three kinds of wavelengths in the sun's rays—A, B and C. Ultra-Violet light A penetrates into the dermis and can result in life-long damage. Originally it was thought that UVA rays were not as harmful as the dangerous UVBs. Recent discoveries indicate that both UVA and UVB waves are harmful to the skin. UVBs are high-energy waves which stimulate the melanin-producing cells—melanocytes—to produce additional melanin. This makes the skin darker. It is now thought that UVB rays also inhibit our immune systems and that sunscreens don't offer the necessary preventative qualities. Just another reason to prevent a sunburn by any means available. Heretofore, the UVC rays, the shortest of the sun's UV waves, were stopped by the Earth's ozone layer. With the reported depletion of this layer, we may no longer be afforded protection from UVC rays.

WHAT IS SPF: These almost universally recognized initials stand for *sun-protection factor* and indexes the degree of the product protects against UVB rays. The index ranges from SPF 2 to SPF 50; SPF 15 is the recommended protection for everyone with the possible exception of young children—where a little higher number might be indicated. When you divide the amount of time you can spend in the sun with a sunscreen without causing damage by the amount of time you can be in the sun without a sunscreen you get the SPF number. If, in general, you can spend 15 unprotected minutes in the burning sun before you start to burn, wearing a sun screen of SPF 15, you can spend 15 minutes x #15, or 225 minutes (3 hours and 45 minutes) in that intense sun without burning. Of course, if you go in the water during that time, all bets are off because no sunscreen is 100% waterproof. Even perspiration can cause the sunscreen to "wash away". By the way, there are three types of sunscreens:

- Those that are absorbed into the skin and in turn, absorb UV rays; these contain an ingredient known as anthranilate and is not as popular as it was ten years ago.

- Products which block the rays of the sun. These sunscreens contain Parsol, also known as arobenzone, which is considered to be the best UVA blocker currently available.

- And, reflectors, like zinc oxide or titanium dioxide. They protect by reflecting ultraviolet rays away from the skin.

Incidentally, sunscreens labels can claim to be *water-resistant* if they protect through 40 minutes of swim-time. *Waterproof* sunscreens must hold up for an hour and twenty minutes of swimming. To protect the body under the swimsuit even further, manufacturers have developed nylon-based fabrics which claim to provide an SPF 30 for use in bathing suits. Although I haven't seen them in the stores as yet, I've heard they'll be commercially available shortly.

QUICK TIP: Since hair is also affected by the sun, being lightened or faded by its rays, try mascara on your lashes. It will make your eyes look great and help them keep their natural color. And, unless you're a Natural Scandinavian blonde whose hair looks more glorious when it's sun streaked, wear a head covering to avoid brassy highlighting. You can also use the sun's heat to help condition your hair. With the rest of you covered, from face to toes, wet your hair and apply generous quantities of a thick, creamy hair conditioner. Sit in the sun for about a half hour. Incidentally, olive oil will also work. If the hair shafts are in good condition but you have split ends, wet the ends and slather with conditioner. Wrap a bandanna around your head, or wear a hat with a small brim. Leave the creamed ends exposed to the sun's warming rays. Either way, after 30 minutes, shampoo thoroughly, rinse with cool water, to close the hair cuticles.

PHOTO-SENSITIVE PROBLEMS: Certain chemicals and extracts are known as photosensitizers. They can cause brown spots on your skin if you wear them when you're sunning yourself. It's a good idea to stay away from any citrus-based products when you're heading into the sun; that includes anything scented with lemon, lime, grapefruit, bergamot and neroli. Your best bet is to omit fragrances during daylight hours when you're heading into the sun's turf. Be careful with other products that contain fragrances—soaps, shampoos, cosmetics and creams. Birth control tablets, as well as some antihistamines or antibiotics can also be the culprits when it comes to developing unsightly discoloration after heavy-duty exposure to the sun. Checking with your physician would be a good precaution if you're taking any medication at all. Women who are pregnant should also be careful. Sun worshipping can increase the chance of getting chloasma—where the skin ends up with blotches or discoloration.

WHAT ABOUT NOT-LIVER SPOTS: Most of you are already aware that liver spots are not connected to the liver, nor with age; but rather are the result of too much time in the sun. Incidentally, those fading creams you may have read about in the small ads in women's magazines, do offer some relief. Hydroquinone is the name of the active ingredient they contain. A patch test, such as that hairstylists are instructed to use before they color your hair, should be performed. Just follow the instructions on the label. It does take time to fade the brown spots and they will probably not disappear altogether. Of course, going back out into the sun defeats the purpose of using a fading cream in the first place.

WHAT TO DO IF (&^%$_)*%$%$&: That means "What can I do if I disregarded your advice and burned my skin to a crisp?"

- For relief from the burning sensation caused by over-exposure to the sun, brew up a batch of tea—as strong as you can get it. Cool it down in a basin or large bowl, using ice cubes. Immerse a soft towel in the brew and spread the towel all over the sun-burned areas.
- Doctor's generally advise taking two aspirin before the red develops after sun ray exposure. The aspirin slows down the skin's inflammation process and also acts to alleviate the pain. In the event that you've let yourself become dehydrated, don't take the aspirin. Instead, drink lots of cold water.

♦ You listened to part of my warnings: used a sun-screen and exposed your skin to the sun's rays gradually. Now you have a tan, your vacation is over and you want to keep the tan as long as you can. Keep it moist with moisturizing lotions. And, to slowdown the peeling process, apply—liberally—warm melted cocoa butter.

VICTORIAN IDEA: Apparently some Victorian ladies also liked the idea of basking in the sun. It was suggested that the following recipe for sun burnt skin be prepared in the Spring, so it would be on hand for use after Summer outings to the surf.

1 Quart of Rain Water
20 Drops of Lavender Essential Oil or
2 hands full of dried Lavender
20 Drops of Rose Essential Oil or
2 hands full of Rose Petals

Mix all of the ingredients and store in a dark-colored stoppered bottle for a fortnight. If using dried flowers, strain liquid through a clean cloth. Shake well before applying to sun burned skin. Repeat application as needed. Since Lavender is reputed to have healing qualities, it might be worth preparing this concoction to soothe the skin after too much of our 20th Century sun.

SUMMER HAIR-COLORING IDEAS: If you're heading for a two-week paradise island type vacation and normally have your hair colored, try this at the last salon appointment before you leave. Ask your colorist to give you your usual color—but two or three shades darker than your usual shade. That way, by the second week of the sun's oxidation, your hair color will not be brassy—but rather, it will be close to your usual pre-vacation color.

The next trick looks best if your hair is dark blonde or light brown. Prepare a glass full of freshly squeezed lemon juice. Add a Tablespoon of any kind of salad oil. Dip your comb into the juice and comb it through the top layer of your hair and sit in the sun for about an hour and a half. Keep repeating the application as soon as your upper hair strands feel dry. Your hair will end up looking as if you spent the better part of $100 in an exclusive salon to get such a natural-looking high-lighting. When asked who did your haircolor—just smile and pretend you don't want to reveal the name of this very special magician.

COVER-UPS: Whatever you choose to cover-up your bathing suit while you're sitting in the sun, make sure it's not polyester. Polyester shirts or caftans cling to the skin and do not let perspiration evaporate easily. Your best buy for comfort and protection is a natural fiber, such as cotton or linen. These fabrics "breathe" and consequently minimize heat and perspiration.

VITAMINS FOR SUNBURN: Vitamin E, which is found in wheat germ oil, helps in the healing of sunburns. It also contains qualities which help prevent blistering. It's a good idea to massage some Vitamin E salve or wheat germ oil into scar tissue before, during and after your stint in the sun.

SUNSCREEN TIPS: Unless you're using a reflective sunscreen, like zinc oxide, you should slather on the product about 20 minutes before you expose your skin to the sun. You can put zinc oxide on moments before you go out. Following are times when you should be extra careful and apply sunscreen extra often and in extra-large quantities:

- ◆ Summers between 10:00 am and 3:00 pm.
- ◆ In the mountains or at altitudes where the thin atmosphere permits more of the suns rays to hit your skin.
- ◆ Because water, in liquid or solid form, are very reflective, if you're going to be sailing, land or water-skiing, swimming or fishing.
- ◆ At beaches between the Tropic of Cancer and the Tropic of Capricorn. (And you thought you'd never have need of that information when you sat in your grade school geography class.)

CHAPTER NINE
FRAGRANCE

"That all women (who) shall from and after such Art seduce and betray into matrimony any of His Majesty's subjects by Scents shall incur the penalty of law against witchcraft and that (said) marriage shall stand null and void."

- excerpted from a 1770 Act of Parliament

Fortunately the 1770 Act of the English Parliament penalizing perfumed women for enticing men through the use of delicious fragrances, has gone the way of most such restrictive laws, and the perfume industry, which came into its own early in the Twentieth Century, is alive and well.

The art of personal and residence scenting had its beginnings many centuries ago, in ancient China where perfumes were very costly to make. To get an acceptable aroma took great talent; exotic ingredients were imported from exotic places at great cost; formulas were kept secret and were passed down to a select few, from generation to generation. In most early cultures, perfumes, in the form of powders and oils were used to honor ancestors, at the feet of the gods, to treat diseases, aromatize banquet areas and by men and women for personal grooming and for purposes of attracting the opposite sex. Some of the scents known as early as the 5th through 1st Centuries B.C. which are still in use today are rose, jasmine, sandalwood, musk and patchouli.

In Arabia, a host would waft perfume in sensers over the heads of guests who were out-staying their welcome, as a hint that they should say "Good Night" and go home. In Persia and in some of the eastern-most Mediterranean countries, rose water was used in cooking and as a medicine, as well as for a perfume. The hieroglyphics in Egypt and the tools found in the tombs, indicated that perfumery was a thriving custom in the days of Tutankhamon, Hatshepshut, Nerfertiti and Cleopatra. Incidentally, the perfume jar found in King Tut's tomb retained its original fragrance some 2200 years. Now that's a long-lasting perfume. There was even a God of Fragrance, by the name of

Nefertem, who is frequently depicted arising from the fragrant and beautiful lotus blossom. Room scenting probably had its real beginnings in Egypt where a sacred perfume made of 16 herbs and flowers was used as an incense to keep the home fragrant overnight.

One of the ancient world's seven great wonders, was Nebuchad-nezzar's Hanging Gardens of Babylon which were filled with fragrant flowers and herbs. At that time, perfumes were already being kept in glass containers and were used to scent the entire body. At a somewhat later date, Alexander the Great had his floors sprinkled with perfume and burned aromatics throughout his residences. In 295 B.C. a Greek man of science, Theophrastus, wrote "Concerning Odors", a paper in which he described the properties of perfumes, how they were made and all about oils as "carriers" for the scents. Women in these times were also well-known perfumers. The best-selling blends of the day—some named for their ingredients and some for their creators—were *Megallum, Mendesion, Nardinum, Susinan, Rhodinum* and *Metopium* (perhaps a forerunner of a popular current-day fragrance). In Alexandria, perfume workers were forced to remove their clothing each evening as they left work, being searched to make sure they hadn't absconded with any of the costly ingredients used in the manufacture of perfume. And, by the year 300-A.D., tax-collectors had discovered *aromatophles*—perfume dealers as a source of revenue.

By the time Nero governed Rome, room scenting was so advanced that he was able to have silver pipes installed at the perimeter of his banquet rooms, through which essences were sprayed. Fountains splashing perfume were to be found throughout the residence. And, as if that weren't enough, the wings of doves were coated with aromatics; the birds were then released over the diners' heads, fluttering fragrance throughout the hall.

The French also got into the perfume business rather early. In 1190 A.D., records show that patents were being granted for perfumes. To become a perfume master, one had to spend four years as an apprentice and another three years as a journeyman. Catherine de Medici, who married Henry the II in 1533, became the patroness of perfuming in France. Her interest and influence encouraged the dominance of French perfumes throughout Europe. By the time Louis XV was in power, it was quite the rage to wear a different perfume every day. The extravagance of such French women as Madame Pompadour was legendary. Even after the Revolution, Napoleon's Josephine was just as ardent and extravagant a devotee of perfume as the notorious Madame. Incidentally, Josephine's favorite aromatic aphrodisiac (or perhaps it was Napoleon's) was musk. Musk is still a scent which denotes sensuality today.

SELECTING A FRAGRANCE

Choosing a perfume is not something one should leave to a mate, a friend or a lover. It's a very personal decision. A scent can make you feel sexy, confident, on top of the world. Unbeknownst to yourself, it can also put you in an irritable mood, or make you blue. Women generally purchase a fragrance for one of three reasons, or a combination of all three.

+ because a marketing campaign leads them to believe that it is a fashionable fragrance
+ because they smelled and liked the fragrance on someone else
+ because it's a classic, and therefore a "safe" choice

However, the best way to select a scent is to use these two criteria:

+ how does it smell on you, and
+ does it get the results you want

It is definitely not a good idea to buy a fragrance, or reject it, on the first whiff. When you first smell a fragrance, what is known as the "top note", will hit your olfactory senses quickly and disappear even more quickly. The "middle" and "low" notes are the ones that determine how the scent will smell after you've worn it for a while. Incidentally, when you intend to find a new cologne or perfume for yourself, do not go to the fragrance department wearing a scent on your wrists or anywhere else on your clothing.

Since there are literally thousands of perfumes, it's not such an easy task to find one that pleases you in every way. If you're like I am, there was a time when you had at least a dozen different perfume bottles on your dresser, having bought them and, after several wearings, discovered they were not exactly what you had in mind. One way to narrow down your search is to find out into which family your favorite scents fall and then find another fragrance from that same family. There are seven families of scents in the feminine group of perfumes; however two of them—Leather & Tobacco and

Fougere—are used primarily for men's fragrances. These are the five families most frequently used to create women's perfumes:

1. Floral scents are generally lighter than other scents, with the exception of jasmine and rose. There are four varieties of floral scents: purely floral, sweet floral, fruity floral, fresh floral.

2. Green scents are a blend of citrus flavors, herbs and mosses and have a sharper, outdoor-sy fragrance.

3. Aldehydic scents have two varieties - aldehydic floral and aldehydic woodsy.

4. Chypre scents are considered to be very sophisticated and have been traced back to the Crusades. The top notes carry the fragrance of citrus; its middle notes contain rose and/or jasmine; the low notes feature such scents as patchouli and musk.

5. Oriental scents evoke thoughts of the exotic, spicy and warm.

Now, when you go hunting for a new fragrance for yourself, first find out into which precise category your current favorite falls. Then seek out other fragrances in that family and variety. Most of the sales representatives at the fragrance counters in the better department and specialty stores have such information at their fingertips or can obtain it for you.

Here are some more ideas to help you with fragrances.

USE ADS AS A CLUE: Many times, a new perfume's advertising will give you a good indication of what the fragrance is all about. It's pretty easy to guess that an ad which features a sultry-looking women in a leopard skin lurking behind a lush tropical flower will not be an ad for a perfume that smells like lilies- of-the-valley or lilacs. On the other hand, if the ad depicts a model in a white sleeveless dress, sniffing a miniature white rosebud, surrounded by a field of wildflowers, you could take a good guess that the town's femme fatale will not choose that fragrance as her signature scent.

YOUR SKIN CAN BE AN INDICATOR: If your skin is on the dry side, fragrances will disappear faster on you than on your oilier-skinned sisters. Because of this faster evaporation rate, you can wear a stronger fragrance. Dark-skinned women can use a fragrance with lighter notes in all ranges because the skin's oils will warm the perfume. As a result the scent lasts longer. Most redheads are better off with fragrances that are not too sweet and not too green.

THREE A DAY: I'd suggest that you limit your fragrance testing to three perfumes a day. More than that and the sensors in your nose will be on over-load. Also, don't put one fragrance on top of another. Try one behind your ear; a second on your left upper arm; and, the third sprayed on your right wrist. Don't put all three on simultaneously. Try one; do some shopping; come back after about twenty minutes and try another; have lunch and then go back for a third pass at the perfume counter. After another scouting trip through the store, if you like one of the three scents, go back and ask for a free sample. If there is none available, purchase the very smallest quantity of eau de toilette or cologne they have available. Then, wear it for a few days to find out if you really like it, if your mate is attracted to it, and your friends ask "What is that great perfume you're wearing?" If it meets all three factors, buy a large size of the cologne and a small bottle of the perfume. If, not, it's back to the fragrance counter to try again.

WHAT A DIFFERENCE A DAY MAKES: Fragrances do smell different on different people. They can also smell different on the same people. A fragrance that's perfect in the morning may become too strong at another time of day. What you eat—particularly strongly scented foods, like garlic, cabbage, onions, and very spicy foods—can affect the way your perfume smells. Whether it's the scent per se, your nose or a combination of both is sometimes difficult to tell. When you stop smoking (if you still are), your scent will definitely smell different. In fact until you've been off "the weed" for a few weeks, even your own personal body scent will seem unfamiliar to you.

THAT TIME OF THE MONTH: Your olfactory senses are most discerning around the time you ovulate and less sensitive to aromas when you're menstruating. The Pill causes changes in your body chemistry and consequently changes in the way your perfume smells. Most medications can alter the way scents smell on you, as well as affect your sense of smell. Although I haven't read anything on the subject, I would imagine with the major changes that take place during menopause, there would be changes in your perfume's scent on your skin, as well.

WHAT'S THE DIFFERENCE?: What makes perfumes different from cologne and eau de toilette?

- Cologne or Eau de Cologne, originally mixed with water from Koln (Cologne), a city in Germany on the Rhine River
  + 3 - 5% concentration of fragrance essence
  + is more water than alcohol
  + good for a body splash

- Eau de Toilette
  + 4 - 8 % concentration of fragrance essence
  + its base is either all alcohol or a mixture of alcohol and water
  + may be used at all the pulse points

- Perfume
  + 15 - 30 % concentration of fragrance essence
  + the base is entirely alcohol
  + to be used sparingly at pulse points

As you can imagine, the perfume is the most expensive of the three fragrance forms. There are some costly perfumes which include a delicate blend of as many as 800 ingredients. With more than 4,000 ingredients available for creating a perfume, it takes great skill and a talented "nose" to design a fragrance which will please many women. The only thing the perfumer can't factor into his/her equation is what your body heat and body chemistry will do to his/her formula. That's why perfume-making is such an art and why good, long-lasting, well-accepted perfumes are so expensive. For every perfume that makes it in the marketplace, a great many fall by the wayside. And, because tastes change, fragrances that are popular in one decade will go into oblivion ten years later. It is extremely difficult to develop a new perfume that will "make it" on today's fashion scene.

WHY ON THE PULSE POINTS & WHERE ARE THEY, ANYWAY: Pulse points are the places where your pulse can be taken—basically where the veins or arteries carry the blood close to the skin's surface. Perfume dabbed on these areas will develop your scent to its fullest. The most popular pulse points for spraying fragrances are: the inside of the wrists, behind the ears, inside the elbows and behind the knees, on the throat, on the ankles, beneath the breasts, at the temples, around the neckline, especially at the nape of the neck. Another great spot for spraying a scent is on the inner thigh—although this is not a recognized pulse point. And cologne sprayed on your feet, sure makes them feel good! A trick women have been using for centuries in one variation or another—saturate a cotton ball with your fragrance and place it between your breasts, held in place by your bra.

MIX 'N' MATCH: To maximize your fragrance, use other products which contain the same or a compatible scent. This is sometimes called "fragrance layering". Applying a coordinated bath oil, especially while your skin is still bath or shower moist, to your pulse points before you spray perfume or cologne, will give the fragrance more staying power. This is an especially helpful trick for dry-skinned women, whose fragrances generally dissipate more rapidly than they do on normal or oily-skinned women. In addition to using a complementary bath oil consider using matching soap, dusting powder and body lotion. Just be sure that you don't use conflicting scents. Incidentally, don't leave your scent spraying to the last minute. Spray about fifteen minutes before you walk out the door. Your fragrance needs time to work its way into your skin and to blend with the skin's chemistry.

TOO MUCH?: Have you ever over-sprayed and ended up trying to figure out a way to get away from yourself. You don't have to make yourself late for an appointment waiting for the scent to evaporate. Just dab a cotton ball moistened with alcohol on the over-sprayed area and be on your way.

HOME ENVIRONMENT SCENTING

Before you started this chapter, you may have thought that room sprays, closet pomanders and bathroom deodorizers were 20th Century inventions; Now you know the practices have been around for five thousand or more years. Here are one-and-a-half dozen things you can do to make your surroundings more fragrant. By the way, the essential oils I mention, are available at most health food stores and at many bath and bedroom boutiques.

1. Dab some essential oil or another favorite scent on your lightbulbs. When the bulb is lit, the scent will be activated and a pleasant

aroma will waft throughout the area. A different scent in each room makes your home even more interesting.

- Cinnamon or Neroli in the dining room
- Pine in the den
- Bergamot in the guest bathroom
- Rose or Jasmine in the bedroom—unless you're in the mood to go right to sleep—in which case, use Lavender
- Rosewood or Clary Sage in the living room
- Sandalwood in the master bathroom

2. Spray your pillowcases with a light fragrance and dust your sheets with a similar bath powder. You could also put a few drops of your favorite essential oil in the final rinse cycle when washing your bed linens.

3. Still have an ironing basket—spray your ironing board, the lining of the ironing basket, your slips, panties, nightgowns, bras and camisoles, with a light cologne.

4. Have a fireplace. Once the fire is roaring, toss in a cup full of pot pourri. Another trick—line up cinnamon, cloves, pine needles or twigs and/or mint leaves on the top-most log and light your fire. Delicious. Lemon and orange rinds handled the same way, add a nice fresh citrus-y aroma to the atmosphere of the room.

5. If you use artificial flowers in your home, try scenting them with a floral essence—a floral bouquet or individual fragrances that match the flower on display. How about Rose Water for rosebuds, Neroli for blossoms, Lily of the Valley for any small white flower, etcetera. Nowadays they make the artificial flowers so real-looking that you almost have to touch them to be sure. With a floral spray, everyone will just think "Of course they're real".

6. Before you put the distilled water into your steam iron, add a few drops of Lavender, Rose or Mandarin and then iron your tablecloths, placemats, napkins and other household linens.

7. Humidifiers can spread delightful fragrance throughout your rooms during the heating dry-out season. Just add a few drops of essentials oils like Mint, Clary Sage, Patchouli or Bergamot to the water, depending on which scents you prefer.

8. When hand-washing your delicate lingerie, add some of the cologne you use most often to the last rinse water. Your drawers (pardon the pun) will smell great.

9. When you've used the last of a perfume or essential oil, open the bottle and pop it-into your lingerie drawers until the last whiff of fragrance has disappeared.

10. Potpourri in jars, bowls, vases make a terrific visual and aromatic addition to any room. Make them yourself or purchase them ready-made. Any time someone sends you a bouquet of roses—and I hope you get them for your birthday, your anniversary, Valentine's Day, Mother's and/or Grandmothers Day and lots of other days throughout the year—save the petals in a bowl until they're dried. Add them to an existing potpourri or start a new one. If the scent is not as strong as you'd like it to be, add a few drops of essential oil, Rose or Rosewood. You'll probably have to replenish the aroma throughout the year anyway. Some other flowers you might consider: carnation, freesia, chrysanthemum, hyacinth and narcissus, lilacs, lilies of the valley and lavender. If you're going to be drying lots of petals, spread them on a window screen or on a cheesecloth. Keep them away from the sun or the pretty colors will fast become too faded. When you're ready to assemble the potpourri, add nutmeg, dried orange, lemon or lime peels, cinnamon and/or cloves. While your at it, put some of this mixture into a small muslin sack, tie it with a metallic cord and hang it over the bar in your closet.

11. Scented soap balls or squares, when gauze-wrapped and ribbon-tied, make a very pleasant sachet for your scarf and glove drawer. By the way, in Elizabethan times, perfuming gloves was a fad following by royalty and commoners alike.

12. If your candles are not scented, as the wax puddles around the base, add a few-drops of any essential oil. How about Lemon for a yellow candle; Mandarin for an orange one; Sandalwood for a brown taper; naturally, pine for the green candle; and Rose or Cinnamon for the bright red one. Just let your imagination run wild.

13. Stationery can be scented to remind people of you. Just spray your favorite fragrance on a cotton ball and drop it into the box with your letterheads and envelopes. Don't have a box. Put some

sheets of your writing paper and envelopes in a large plastic "zip and seal" bag with that fragrant cotton ball and let them "marinate" together for a few days. You could use one kind for romantic words, another kind for a letter to the complaint department at the local store. Ylang-Ylang and Melissa are supposed to calm down angry moods.

14. Spray a fresh-smelling scent on your quilted hangers. You might try a heady sensuous fragrance for the hangers which hold a sequined jacket and a light flowery scent for a pretty summer blouse.

15. Tuck a cotton ball you've sprayed with cologne into the cardboard tube in your roll of toilet paper or paper towels.

16. Six to eight drops of essential oil on a cotton ball left with your wrapping paper overnight, will add a pleasant dimension to your gift-giving. Again, vary the scent for the occasion. Something floral for Mother's Day; Pine for Christmas; Rose for a June wedding or birthday and so on.

17. A few drops of essential oil on the pin cushion for your sewing box will make your mending chores more pleasant. Here too you can vary the fragrance by season.

18. Many mid-Eastern recipes call for Rose or Neroli Water (Orange Blossom). Why not get a bit adventurous and try one of them.

FINAL THOUGHTS AND FEELINGS FROM ADRIEN ARPEL

I believe beauty can be ageless and timeless and that it should be effortless to maintain. That is why I've written this book, dear Reader, to help you learn how to look younger, healthier and more attractive the Arpel way.

Some women exude confidence and have an inner strength which makes them appear outwardly beautiful, even though their features and figures are far from perfect, and they are long past the accepted age for entering beauty contests. These special women have learned how to use life's experiences and their years of knowledge in a positive way. They have developed a comfort level about their appearance which allows them to project themselves as ageless and beautiful. I believe when you give off positive, confident, beautiful vibes, everyone around you thinks of you that way.

In the many years that I have worked directly with these fabulous women, I have been taught a lot, which has greatly influenced the way I look and think today. I've shared my learning experiences with you chapter by chapter, and I firmly believe *dreams never die;* they simply age just as we do. Like the subtle changes that take place on the body and face with each passing year, we have to modify our dreams, making subtle changes that enable us to make them a reality no matter what our chronological age. Let me give you some examples of what I mean. I have a customer/friend who, since she was a little girl, wanted to be a ballet dancer. She married at an early age, had children and when they grew up and fled the nest, she believed her dream was long gone. One day while reading the local paper, she noticed that the professional Ballet Company in her community was looking for a "Gal Friday"—someone to do anything and everything related to the dance company. She applied; but instead of submitting a resume showing skills and experience which she didn't have, she enthusiastically spoke of her love of ballet and how she had read everything on the subject that she could get her hands on and during the past twenty years had seen most of the company's productions. She explained that she would be delighted to do anything asked of her and that she just wanted to be involved with "dance". She really did have years of experience; just not in the traditional sense of "marketable" skills. Her enthusiasm was contagious. She was hired and today, (3 years later), she is in a management position with The Ballet Company, finally realizing her "dream" . . . not in its original form . . . but close enough to fulfill her.

Another customer/friend who many years ago worked to help her husband through college and get started in his career, has now, 20 years later, gotten him to return the favor. She always dreamed of having a degree and in a relatively short period of time she'll be receiving it. There is another friend who always wanted to attend a university but her early marriage and babies made that impossible until recently. Now, however, she doesn't want the pressure of matriculating; so she's taking art appreciation courses, with the goal of obtaining an interesting job in an art gallery or a museum. She is building her confidence through the acquisition of knowledge and I believe is well on her way to becoming a confident, ageless, beautiful woman who will realize her dream.

Every young girl's dream is to be the prettiest girl in her class. If you are lucky, you are born with the right chromosomes. If not, that dream fades fast. It need not. I believe you can be the best looking woman in your class (not referring to school) simply by taking this book seriously and working on looking and feeling terrific for your age, no matter what or where your starting point is, so please read, re-read and refer to this book often.

To make a simple analogy. We don't put weeds in vases, we put fresh flowers and *every woman is a flower*. We all bloom but at different times of our lives; so to all the late bloomers out there, you have plenty of time to learn, grow, and flower.

Remember, in today's world, age is just a number and, if you believe the best is yet to come . . . the best *is* yet to come.

BIBLIOGRAPHY

Adrien Arpel, *Adrien Arpel's 851 Fast Beauty Fixes and Facts*, Dell 1985

Adrien Arpel, *How To Look Ten Years Younger*, Rawson Wade, 1981

Adrien Arpel, *Adrien Arpel's Three-Week Crash Makeover/Shapeover Beauty Program*, Rawson Associates 1977

Charla Devereux & Bernie Hephrun, *The Perfume Kit*, Macmillan 1995

Deborah Hutton, *Vogue Beauty for Life*, Crown 1994

Frances Kennett, *History of Perfume*, Harrap 1975

Jan Laarkey, *Flatter Your Figure*, Simon & Schuster 1991

Darlene Mathis, *Women of Color*, Ballentine 1994

Felicia Milewica & Lois Joy Johnson, *The Beauty Editor's Workbook*, Random House 1983

Jan Moran, *Fabulous Fragrances*, Crescent House 1994

Angela Partington, *The Oxford Dictionary of Quotations*, Oxford University Press 1992

David Ryback, *Look 10 Years Younger, Live 10 Years Longer*, Prentiss Hall 1995

And select articles from the following publications:

Anton Community Newspapers, Family Circle, Good Housekeeping, Ladies Home Journal, Mademoiselle, McCalls, New Woman, Newsday, Redbook, Self, Shape, Vogue, Weight Watchers Magazine

Looking Younger

Sunday, March 29, 1981   LAS VEGAS SUN   5A

Page 2, Section 8   Houston Chronicle   Wednesday, January 13, 1982

At right: Adrien Arpel, right, gives Pam Materka chin and throat acupressure, facial exercise to prevent and alleviate double chin.

...Materka awaits Adrien Arpel mini facial exercises.

No miracles here
There's no magic wand to wave, just a good skincare regimen to use

BY HARRIET EDLESON
Chronicle Staff

WHEN ADRIEN ARPEL moves, you watch, captivated by the fringe of her bangs, the endlessly long, thick lashes that encircle her eyes, and the quick...

...women find ...and image

LOS ANGELES TIMES   Fashion82   FRIDAY, MARCH 19, 1982

arpel: reading your face map
BY PADDY CALISTRO

FOCUS

The Dothan Eagle
Sunday, October 17, 1983   Section C

Adrien Arpel
REPACKAGE YOURSELF
faces

Learning what goes where helps you put on your best

extra/fashion

Skin care adv...
by CAROL TEEGARDIN

...goes where ...her a... success